An Inorganic Chemistry Monograph
Consultant Editor: H. G. Heal, The Queen's University, Belfast

THE ALLOTROPY OF
THE ELEMENTS

Oldbourne Chemistry Series

The Allotropy of the Elements

W. E. ADDISON, B.Sc., Ph.D., F.R.I.C.

University of Nottingham

AMERICAN ELSEVIER PUBLISHING
COMPANY, INC.

52 Vanderbilt Ave., New York, N.Y. 10017

OLDBOURNE BOOK CO. LTD.
121 Fleet Street, London, E.C.4

© *Oldbourne Book Co. Ltd. 1964*

PRINTED IN GREAT BRITAIN BY
SPOTTISWOODE, BALLANTYNE AND CO. LTD.
LONDON AND COLCHESTER

PREFACE

To many chemists, the term 'allotropy' brings to mind the elements sulphur and phosphorus, and then, perhaps, tin and carbon; it comes as a surprise to realize that almost one-half of the known elements can exist in more than one form in the solid state. Such a common phenomenon is clearly worthy of study.

The study of allotropy requires an understanding of various branches of chemistry—of chemical bonding and crystal structure, thermodynamics and the Phase Rule, to mention the more important. The main emphasis in this text is upon the structural aspects of the subject since these are the more appropriate to a text in a series devoted to Inorganic Chemistry. Limitations of space, and the standard of treatment preclude a comprehensive discussion.

The book falls into two sections; the first, of three Chapters, devoted to physical aspects, including structure, and the second, comprising Chapters 4 and 5, devoted to a detailed description of the allotropy of the individual elements. In the first section, I have outlined a treatment of chemical bonding appropriate to the elements, in order particularly to interpret differences in physical properties of different allotropes which are dependent upon bond type. It seemed unnecessary to consider different theories of bonding, so that the valence bond approach and Pauling's theory of metals have been excluded.

Whereas the overall standard of the text is appropriate to University level, I hope that much of the description of allotropy, particularly in Chapter 4, will be understandable to sixth formers.

I wish to thank my colleagues, Dr. D. Sutton and Dr. J. H. Sharp, who read the manuscript and offered advice. Some critical selection of subject matter has been necessary, and the ultimate choice has been mine alone. Thanks are due to my wife also for her help and encouragement throughout the preparation of the book, and to Professor H. Krebs for the provision of original material from which I derived much benefit.

February 1964   W. ERIC ADDISON

CONTENTS

Chapter 1

GENERAL DISCUSSION OF ALLOTROPY

INTRODUCTION

The term 'allotropy' is derived from Greek words meaning 'another form', and it was introduced into chemical literature by Berzelius as long ago as 1841, in order to describe the existence of an element or compound in more than one form in the solid state. An example of this which was known at that time is the occurrence of carbon as diamond and charcoal (graphite). Berzelius believed that allotropic forms of elements yielded different materials after chemical reaction, e.g. iron pyrites and marcasite, both of which correspond to the composition FeS_2, were believed to contain different allotropic forms of sulphur. This idea, however, was soon found to be untenable.

A second term, 'polymorphism', which means 'having many forms' is also used to describe the same phenomenon. Often, in practice, the term allotropy is used to describe the existence of elements in different forms whereas the similar behaviour of compounds is described as polymorphism. This distinction is not always drawn, and some authors use one term for both elements and compounds whereas others use the alternative. Buerger, for example, has written: 'The word polymorphism is used to embrace the general relations between the several phases of the same substance without regard to the number of phases involved. The use of a special word (allotropy) represents an unnecessary category and should be dropped in view of the identity of the phenomenon with polymorphism.' Partington makes the same point, 'A distinction between allotropy of elements and polymorphism of compounds is really unnecessary', but, in contrast, prefers the term allotropy.

Since both terms are in such widespread use, it is difficult to imagine that either will ever be abandoned. In the present book the discussion is restricted to the elements, and the term allotropy is used in this narrower sense. Much of the general discussion applies equally to compounds.

It is necessary to define in what respects the different forms, allotropes, of an element differ from each other. In Berzelius' day allotropic modifications could be recognized only by differences in certain physical properties such as colour and density. Such criteria are still used at the present day, but are not always reliable, since colour can be modified by change in particle size or traces of impurities, and accurate determina-

1

tions of the density of finely divided material are often difficult. There are in the literature many claims of the existence of allotropic modifications, which are based on some such doubtful and incomplete evidence; the definite existence of a separate allotrope should be accepted only after the presentation of evidence of a more fundamental kind.

The most reliable criterion of allotropy is the proof, by physical methods of structure determination, of the existence of forms of the element in which there are different arrangements of atoms in the crystal.

Since the atomic arrangements are different, the physical properties of the allotropes are also different. It is perhaps useful to consider the analogy that two or more completely different buildings can be built from exactly the same bricks, or even words of different meaning from the same letters.

Different atomic arrangements can result from a change in the complexity of a molecule, e.g. the existence of sulphur under different conditions as a hexatomic or octatomic molecule, a change in the orientation of molecules of the same size with respect to each other, e.g. rhombic and monoclinic sulphur, both of which contain S_8 molecules, or, in elements such as the metals which do not possess discrete molecules, a different sequence in the stacking of layers of atoms.

Isotopy is, like allotropy, the existence of different forms of an element, but these differences are due to differences in the constitution of various nuclei of the element and have no effect upon atomic positions in a crystal lattice.

Since allotropic modifications differ in the arrangements of their constituent atoms, it follows that they will differ not only in their respective physical properties but also in their energy content (see p. 13). The comment of von Siemens as long ago as 1880 is still apposite: 'Allotropic modifications of an element are composed of one element associated with different proportions of available or potential energy, and consequently they exhibit different physical and chemical properties.' Allotropy can be studied, therefore, from both a structural and an energetic viewpoint. Since this text is one of a series which discusses, particularly, Inorganic Chemistry, and is intended to reach only a modest standard, the structural aspects will receive rather more emphasis than the energetic aspects.

For the purpose of the present text, the allotropy of an element is defined as the existence of an element in at least two different forms in the solid state where the constituent atoms are arranged in different ways in the different forms. This definition would be more rigorous if it required each individual solid form to be crystalline. Crystallinity requires a regular ordering of atoms throughout the entire material and

2

can be confirmed experimentally by X-ray methods (see below). The absence of long-range order in the atomic arrangement is a feature of a polymerization product where the conditions of formation do not allow perfect alignment of polymeric fragments, and different chain lengths, degrees of cross-linking, etc., are obtained. The elements phosphorus, selenium, etc., can be obtained in such a non-crystalline, or amorphous, state. Since there is incomplete order, different preparations of these materials have different physical properties; they cannot be said to be well defined or well characterized, and it is a matter of debate whether such a material merits recognition as an allotropic species.

The term allotropy was introduced originally to describe behaviour in the solid state. Some authors have continued to use it in this sense, whereas others have applied it to elements which can exist in different degrees of aggregation in the liquid and gaseous states also, and the derivation of the term does not preclude this. The definition given above is limited to the narrower sense since this is probably the more generally accepted usage. The liquid and gaseous states are referred to only when this assists an understanding of the solid state.

Although *ortho-* and *para-*hydrogen and active nitrogen are not allotropes within the terms of the above definition, these different forms of the elements are discussed since they are of chemical significance.

The understanding of allotropy has advanced appreciably since Berzelius's day, yet many gaps in knowledge and understanding remain, and many experimental difficulties have yet to be overcome. However, the perusal of this text will show a situation very different from that described years ago by W. S. Jevons: 'What are allotropic states? Curious states which chemists frequently dispose of by calling them allotropic, a term frequently used when they are puzzled to know what has happened.'

EXPERIMENTAL APPROACHES

New allotropes must be recognized and allotropic transformations studied by the use of physical techniques; it has been pointed out above that allotropes differ in their physical properties.

Diffraction Methods. Probably the most useful technique is that of X-ray diffraction, since different arrangements of atoms produce different X-ray diffraction patterns. This method can be applied to a single crystal, to a powdered sample of crystalline material, or to amorphous material. These can be considered in turn.

The detailed study of diffraction patterns from a single crystal allows a complete determination of the positions of all the atoms in the crystal, and hence interatomic distances (bond lengths) and interbond angles.

3

Ultimately, of course, it is very desirable to have such complete structural information about all materials, and from this a complete proof of allotropy can result. A complete structure determination is a lengthy process, however, and would seldom be attempted as a first step to show that an allotropic change had taken place.

At an early stage in the analysis of a single crystal, it is possible to determine the size and 'shape' of the unit cell, i.e. the smallest building brick from which the entire crystal can be constructed by infinite repetition. Knowledge of the details of the unit cell can characterize a particular allotropic modification, since it is most unlikely that two materials can have exactly the same unit cell. In this unlikely situation a comparison of the intensities of the various reflections of the diffraction patterns obtained would reveal differences if the arrangements of atoms in the unit cells were indeed different, as required by allotropy. A description of the unit cell tells little about the detailed atomic arrangement; the 'shape' is important, since allotropic modifications are frequently differentiated by differences in this property.

A unit cell is defined by quoting the lengths of the three axes, and the angles between them. In many cases one or more of the interaxial angles is $90°$, and sometimes two or even all three axial lengths are equal. Such conditions as these define the system to which the crystal belongs, i.e. the 'shape' of the unit cell. These systems are listed below, with their required characteristics; a, b and c denote the axial lengths, and α, β and γ the interaxial angles.

Cubic	$a = b = c,$	$\alpha = \beta = \gamma = 90°$
Tetragonal	$a = b \neq c,$	$\alpha = \beta = \gamma = 90°$
Hexagonal	$a = b \neq c,$	$\alpha = \beta = 90°, \quad \gamma = 120°$
Rhombohedral	$a = b = c,$	$\alpha = \beta = \gamma \neq 90°$
Orthorhombic	$a \neq b \neq c,$	$\alpha = \beta = \gamma = 90°$
Monoclinic	$a \neq b \neq c,$	$\alpha = \gamma = 90°, \quad \beta \neq 90°$
Triclinic	$a \neq b \neq c,$	$\alpha \neq \beta \neq \gamma$

As an illustration of the use of these systems in describing allotropes, the best-known forms of sulphur are orthorhombic and monoclinic, whereas a third form is rhombohedral; also the two forms of close-packing found commonly for metallic structures are differentiated by their crystal systems since the one is cubic and the other hexagonal.

It is much more difficult to obtain complete structural information from a powdered specimen than from a single crystal, but, of course, powdered materials are more often available than single crystals. It is sometimes possible to determine the crystal system and even the dimensions of the unit cell. The advantage of the powder method is that it allows a 'fingerprint' of the material to be taken rapidly, and such

4

'fingerprints' can be compared rapidly, thus showing whether two materials are the same or different. No two different materials can ever give identical X-ray powder patterns.

Not every solid is perfectly crystalline, and a number of elements such as selenium, sulphur and phosphorus have forms which are amorphous to X-rays, presumably because of lack of long-range order in their atomic arrangements. The experimentally obtained information from such studies, and from those of liquids also, is shown in the form of radial distribution curves; in these the environment of a given atom is plotted as number of neighbours against distance. Useful information can often be deduced from these plots, particularly when comparison is made with curves to be expected for known crystal structures.

The diffraction of neutrons and electrons are also used to obtain structural information, but are less important than X-rays. Electron diffraction is used mainly for gaseous materials, and neutron diffraction is particularly valuable for the detection of light atoms in the presence of heavy ones.

Physical Methods based on Differences in Energy Content. The absorption of electromagnetic radiation corresponding to various regions of the spectrum can be studied. Radiation really comprises packets of definite energy, so that the absorption of a particular wavelength indicates that there is a transition of an electronic, rotational or vibrational nature in the irradiated material, the energy of which corresponds to that of the absorbed radiation. The possible transitions vary according to the structural arrangements of the atoms, and the energy content of the material irradiated. Hence absorption spectra can be used as 'fingerprints' as can X-ray powder patterns. More quantitative information about the shapes of molecules, bond strengths, etc., can also be obtained in some studies if required.

A change from one allotropic form to another can be compared with a change of state, e.g. from liquid to solid, and is accompanied by a latent heat change. It follows that such transitions should be seen when rate of heating or of cooling is plotted against temperature, when an allotropic change falls within the appropriate temperature range.

A phase change, corresponding to an allotropic transition, can also be detected and its rate studied, by a study of the change of other physical properties which are perhaps less directly related to the energies of the respective allotropes. Examples of such properties are thermal and electrical conductivity, viscosity, density. Reference to the use of these methods will be made where appropriate, in individual cases.

Great care should be exercised in the interpretation of data, and it seems certain that many more allotropic modifications have been claimed to exist than are certainly genuine. Two quotations from a

5

recent paper by Hoard and Newkirk serve to underline these points. First, 'It can be said that published X-ray data have seemed more or less convincingly to support the existence of more than a dozen polymorphs (allotropes). Our analysis has apparently eliminated three of these....' The second quotation illustrates that physical appearance can be misleading, 'Despite the curiously different habits, the needles and the plates (of hexagonal aspect) were shown to have the same tetragonal structure.'

THE PHASE RULE AND ALLOTROPY

An early interest in allotropy was that the Phase Rule could be extended to allotropic substances. The Phase Rule expresses mathematically the relationship between (i) the number of separate phases (P) which exist in a system at equilibrium, (ii) the number of components (C) present in the system, and (iii) the number of degrees of freedom (F), i.e. The number of defining conditions which can be varied without causing a change in the number of phases present. This relationship is:

$$F = C - P + 2$$

A phase is a part of the system which is wholly homogeneous, but is separated from other homogeneous parts of the system by a boundary surface. For any substance, gas, liquid and solid represent three separate phases. The liquid state, if it contains two immiscible liquids, represents two phases, and distinct solids also represent separate phases, whereas the gaseous state is always homogeneous and can be one phase only.

The term 'component' can be difficult to define completely for some systems, but within the scope of the present work, a component can be defined as a constituent of the system. Although the number of components in a system can vary, only one-component systems need to be discussed in a consideration of the application of the Phase Rule to allotropy.

The number of degrees of freedom of a system is the number of factors which can be varied without a change in the number of phases present. These factors are temperature, pressure and the concentration of the components; the last of these is not applicable to all systems. The consequences of degrees of freedom can be understood more clearly from the following discussion.

For a one-component system, the Phase Rule equation reduces to $F = 3 - P$. Hence, if only one phase is present, there are two degrees of freedom, i.e. both temperature and pressure can be altered independently without changing the number of phases in equilibrium. The system is said to be bivariant, and corresponds to an entire region of a $P - T$ diagram (see Fig. 1.1 for this and the subsequent discussion). If

6

two phases are present, there is only one degree of freedom and the system is said to be univariant; thus a change of temperature requires a simultaneous change in the pressure of the system if equilibrium is to be maintained and no change in the number of phases present is to occur, and conversely for a change of pressure. A univariant system is represented by a line on the $P - T$ diagram. Finally, if three phases are present, the system possesses no degrees of freedom and is said to be invariant; thus neither the temperature nor the pressure can be changed without causing the disappearance of one of the phases. Such a system is represented by a point on the $P - T$ diagram.

A One-component System with One Solid Phase. It is appropriate to consider univariance and invariance for a normal one-component system, i.e. one which possesses only one solid phase, before considering a system which shows allotropy, i.e. possesses two solid phases. Three cases of univariance arise in such a system, (i) solid–vapour, (ii) solid–liquid, and (iii) liquid–vapour. These are discussed in turn.

(i) The graphical representation of a system in which solid and vapour can exist together in equilibrium is a curve which originates at the absolute zero of temperature and terminates at the melting point of the solid. It is known as the sublimation curve, is convex towards the temperature axis, and separates two regions where the system is bivariant; these regions define the conditions under which (*a*) the solid and (*b*) the vapour can exist at equilibrium in the absence of a second phase. If the sublimation pressure reaches atmospheric at a temperature below the melting point of the solid, the substance will sublime rather than melt.

(ii) A system in which solid and liquid can exist together in equilibrium is represented by a fusion curve. This inclines either towards or away from the pressure axis according to whether the density of the liquid is greater or less than that of the solid form. The normal melting point of the solid is the temperature on this curve which corresponds to a pressure of one atmosphere. This curve separates the bivariant regions in which the solid and liquid can exist at equilibrium as solitary phases.

(iii) The conditions under which liquid and vapour can exist together in equilibrium are defined by the vaporization curve, which is similar in shape to the sublimation curve, but slopes less steeply in the vicinity of the point at which they intersect. This essential difference can be explained by reference to the Clausius-Clapeyron equation, i.e.

$$\frac{\mathrm{d}P}{\mathrm{d}T} = \frac{q}{T(v_2 - v_1)}$$

where P and T are the pressure and temperature of the system respectively, v_2 and v_1 are the volumes of one gram of the substance under

7

different conditions, and q is the heat (per gram) which is absorbed during the change.

Let v_g be the volume of a given mass of substance in the gaseous state, and v_s and v_l the volumes of the same mass in the solid and liquid states respectively. Now the density of a gas is much less than that of the corresponding solid or liquid, so that v_s and v_l can be neglected in comparison with v_g; hence the volume changes which accompany sublimation and vaporization, i.e. $(v_g - v_s)$ and $(v_g - v_l)$ respectively, can both be represented approximately by v_g.

The slopes of the vaporization and sublimation curves can be written as

$$\left(\frac{\mathrm{d}P}{\mathrm{d}T}\right)_{L \to V} \quad \text{and} \quad \left(\frac{\mathrm{d}P}{\mathrm{d}T}\right)_{S \to V}$$

respectively, and at their point of intersection the temperature, T, is the same for both, and the volume change can be regarded as the same. Hence, the ratio of the slopes of the two curves is given by:

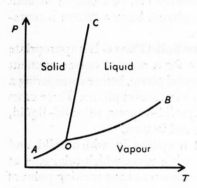

FIG. 1.1. The sublimation curve (*OA*), vaporization curve (*OB*) and fusion curve (*OC*) for an an arbitrary system. The density of the liquid is less than that of the solid.

$$\frac{(\mathrm{d}P/\mathrm{d}T)_{S \to V}}{(\mathrm{d}P/\mathrm{d}T)_{L \to V}} = \frac{q_{S \to V}}{q_{L \to V}}$$

Since the heat required to effect sublimation, $q_{S \to V}$, is greater than that to effect vaporization, $q_{L \to V}$, it follows that the slope of the sublimation curve must be the greater.

The vaporization curve continues to a point at which the density of the vapour and the liquid become the same; above the temperature corresponding to this point, which is called the critical temperature, the liquid cannot exist, and the vapour cannot be liquefied. The pressure corresponding to the critical temperature on the $P - T$ diagram is known as the critical pressure, and is normally very high.

The three curves representing the univariant systems meet at a point (see Fig. 1.1), and at this point all three phases can exist in equilibrium with each other. The system is invariant at this point, since $P = 3$, and hence $F = 0$; i.e. neither temperature nor pressure can be varied without causing one of the phases to disappear. There is only one such point in a simple one-component system; it is defined by definite values of both temperature and pressure, and is known as the triple point since three phases can co-exist at that point.

The Phase Rule approach to a one-component system which possesses only one solid phase has been described in some detail to allow com-

8

parison with its application to a system with two solid phases, i.e. where the solid has two allotropic forms. Before considering such an application, it will be useful to emphasize some points concerning equilibria. First, the Phase Rule, as it has a thermodynamic derivation, states only the number of phases present at equilibrium under various conditions and gives no information about the rate of attainment of equilibrium, or about the mechanism by which a change to or from equilibrium can take place. (A discussion of mechanism and rate follows later pp. 18–26.) Secondly, the Phase Rule can only be applied to allotropic substances in which the change takes place reversibly, i.e. there is a definite temperature at which both forms can exist in equilibrium with each other. Such allotropes are referred to as enantiotropes, and the change from one form to another is said to be an enantiotropic change. There are definite conditions under which each form is stable, although they can sometimes exist under different conditions, when they are said to be metastable, just as, for example, water can be obtained in a supercooled state at a temperature below 0°C, if no nuclei are present to initiate crystallization. An allotrope which passes into another allotrope by a change which cannot be reversed, and where the two forms cannot exist together in equilibrium, is known as a monotropic modification, and the change is a monotropic change. A monotrope is unstable under all attainable conditions.

A One-component System with Two Solid Phases. The application of the Phase Rule to a substance which shows enantiotropy can now be considered. It is convenient to forsake general terms, and to use a specific example for this discussion, and the best-known example is, of course, sulphur which has an enantiotropic change between rhombic and monoclinic forms.

In this one-component system there are four possible phases—vapour, liquid, and rhombic and monoclinic solid forms. In accordance with the Phase Rule it is not possible that all four phases should exist together in equilibrium with each other, since P has a maximum value of three, when C has a value of one. There are four bivariant systems, denoted Vap., Liq., Rhom. and Mono. in Fig. 1.2. Within each of the four regions in the Figure, temperature and pressure can be varied independently without the formation of a new phase.

The number of possible univariant systems corresponds to the number of ways in which two phases can be selected from the total of four, viz. six, and these are as follows: Rhom.—vap., corresponding to the line AB (Fig. 1.2); Mono.—vap., the line BC; Liq.—vap., the line CD; Rhom.—mono., the line BE; Mono.—liq., the line CE; Rhom.—liq., the line EF. Each of these lines represents a system with one degree of freedom, so that a change of temperature requires a change of pressure

9

2

also, if the system is to remain in equilibrium, and conversely for a change of pressure.

Finally, there are four possible invariant systems, corresponding to the number of ways in which three phases can be selected from the total of four. Each of these is represented by a triple point, and they are as follows: Rhom.—mono.—vap., at point B; Mono.—liq.—vap., at point C; Rhom.—mono.—liq., at point E; Rhom.—liq.—vap., at point G. The last of these four is not realized in practice since it lies in the region where all three phases are metastable, and the only stable phase at that point of the diagram is the remaining one, i.e. the monoclinic solid form.

The phase diagram of Fig. 1.2 can now be considered in rather more

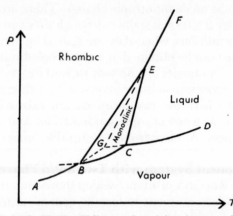

FIG. 1.2. The $P-T$ diagram for sulphur (not to scale).

detail. The curve AB represents equilibrium between rhombic sulphur and sulphur vapour; there is a definite value for the vapour pressure corresponding with every temperature, and a change of temperature requires a change of vapour pressure if equilibrium is to be maintained. This line can be described by an experimentally ascertained equation, i.e.

$$\log p = 11\cdot866 - 5267/T$$

where p is the vapour pressure in mm and T is the absolute temperature.

At the triple point B, both the monoclinic and rhombic forms are in equilibrium with sulphur vapour. The conditions at this invariant point are a pressure of approximately 4×10^{-3} mm and a temperature of $95\cdot5°C$. The transition temperature is that temperature at which the rhombic form is observed to transform into the monoclinic form, at a pressure of one atmosphere; it lies on the transition curve, BE, at a point corresponding to a pressure of one atmosphere, and it is easier to measure the transition temperature than the temperature of the triple point, since

10

it involves experimentation at normal pressure. The difference in temperature between the triple point and the transition temperature can be calculated as follows by use of the Clapeyron-Clausius equation. The density of the monoclinic form of sulphur is less than that of the rhombic form, so that as the rhombic form transforms into the monoclinic, i.e. as heat is supplied to the system, an increase in volume of $0 \cdot 013$ cm^3/g is found. The heat of transition is known to be $2 \cdot 81$ cal/g. Thus, applying the equation:

$$\frac{dP}{dT} = \frac{q}{T(v_2 - v_1)} = \frac{2 \cdot 81 \, \mathrm{cal\,g^{-1}} \times 4 \cdot 18 \times 10^7 \, \mathrm{dyne\,cm\,cal^{-1}}}{368 \cdot 5 \, \mathrm{deg.} \times 0 \cdot 013 \, \mathrm{cm^3\,g^{-1}} \times 981 \, \mathrm{dyne\,g^{-1}}}$$

$$= 24 \cdot 9 \times 10^3 \, \mathrm{g/cm^2/deg.}$$

$$\approx 25 \text{ atmospheres per degree}$$

The change in temperature corresponding to a change in pressure of one atmosphere is thus $0 \cdot 04°$ which is close to the likely experimental error. The temperature of $95 \cdot 5°$ can thus be quoted as that of the triple point and of the transition at normal pressure. It should be noted that the transition temperature and the temperature of the triple point of a system are not usually identical; also, that at the transition temperature the system is univariant and can represent equilibrium between the two solid forms only when no vapour is present, rather than invariant as at the triple point.

The transition curve, *BE*, which gives the variation of the transition temperature with pressure, has the gradient calculated above. It is analogous with the fusion curve in a system in which the solid can exist in only one form. If the density of monoclinic sulphur were greater than that of rhombic sulphur, the sign of $(v_2 - v_1)$ in the above expression would be negative, and the transition curve inclined in the opposite sense with respect to the pressure axis.

The curve *BC* represents the univariant system where monoclinic sulphur is in equilibrium with sulphur vapour. It can, like *AB* and *BE*, be represented mathematically. The point *C* is the triple point at which the monoclinic modification is in equilibrium with both liquid and vapour. This is completely analogous with the triple point in a system where the solid can exist in one form only. The temperature of the triple point at *C* is 119°C, and the pressure is approximately 0·02 mm. As in the change from rhombic to monoclinic sulphur, there is an increase in the volume of the system when monoclinic sulphur melts to give the liquid. The values of $(v_2 - v_1)$ and q for this change are $0 \cdot 029$ cm^3/g and $9 \cdot 14$ cal/g respectively. The line *CE* represents the univariant system where monoclinic sulphur is in equilibrium with the liquid, and is the fusion curve for monoclinic sulphur; in this equilibrium no vapour or rhombic

11

sulphur is present. The slope of CE, i.e. dP/dT, as evaluated by the Clausius-Clapeyron equation using the above data is $38 \cdot 1 \ kg/cm^2/deg.$; it is therefore in the same sense as the slope of the transition curve BE but is more steep, so that the two curves intersect, at E.

The intersection, at E, of the transition curve BE and the fusion curve CE represents a further triple point at which the rhombic and monoclinic forms are in equilibrium with the liquid. It is the maximum temperature at which monoclinic sulphur can exist as a stable form. The temperature and pressure of this point are known with less precision, but are approximately 150°C and 1400 kg/cm^2.

The lines CD and EF represent univariant systems where there is equilibrium between liquid and vapour, the vaporization curve, and between rhombic sulphur and liquid, the fusion curve of rhombic sulphur, respectively.

When a sample of rhombic sulphur is heated up rapidly so that insufficient time is available for the transition to the monoclinic form to be accomplished, it melts at a temperature below the normal melting point which is that of the monoclinic form. If the liquid is maintained at this temperature, it solidifies and on a further elevation of the temperature melts at the 'normal' temperature of 119°C. There is a triple point corresponding to this 'premature' melting point, just as there is such a point corresponding to the melting point of monoclinic sulphur. This triple point corresponds to the invariant system rhombic–liquid–vapour, and since it lies in the region where the only stable phase is the alternative monoclinic form, and the three phases are metastable, no true equilibrium can be observed. This triple point is at G in Fig. 1.2, and lies on the extra polation of both AB and DC, the rhombic–vapour and liquid–vapour univariant systems respectively. The temperature and pressure which define the triple point G are 112·8°C and 0·01 mm respectively, and the curve GE is the transition curve corresponding to the triple point G in the same way as BE corresponds to the point B.

One further feature complicates the behaviour of sulphur. Liquid sulphur is a mixture of molecular forms in equilibrium, and if this is cooled rapidly the solid formed is not identical with that obtained if the cooling is slower (see p. 110 *et seq.*). When chilled to normal temperature it cannot immediately transform into the stable form, and since it has a different structure and physical form, it has different physical properties. Studies of the phase diagram of sulphur must start from material known to be rhombic sulphur, e.g. recrystallized material, to ensure accuracy.

Phase diagrams can be prepared similarly to represent the behaviour of elements other than sulphur, and their interpretation follows similar lines. Such complete information is by no means available in every case. As was pointed out above, the Phase Rule is concerned with the nature of equilibria but gives no information about the rate or mechanism of their attainment. A later section includes a discussion of these aspects of allotropy (p. 18).

THERMODYNAMIC ASPECTS OF ALLOTROPY

The following discussion of allotropic changes is limited, for the sake of simplicity, to those which occur at constant temperature and pressure.

Each phase of a system is characterized by a definite temperature, energy and entropy, and the inter-relationship of these quantities is expressed by the equation first obtained by Gibbs:

$$G = U - TS + PV \tag{1.1}$$

sometimes written as

$$G = H - TS \tag{1.2}$$

where G is the free energy
  U is the internal energy
  S is the entropy,
  T is the temperature,
  P is the pressure,
  V is the volume, and
  $H = U + PV$, is known as the enthalpy or heat content.

The heat content, or enthalpy, of a system increases as the temperature of the system increases. The rate of this increase, which varies according to the temperature range studied, is known as the heat capacity of the system, i.e.

$$C_p = \left(\frac{\partial H}{\partial T}\right)_p \tag{1.3}$$

where C_p, the heat capacity of the system at constant pressure, can be defined as the quantity of heat required to raise the temperature of the system by one degree, while the pressure is maintained constant.

If an element can exist in two different forms, then at any temperature T, let the free energies of the two forms per g-atom be,

$$G_1 = H_1 - TS_1 \tag{1.4}$$

$$G_2 = H_2 - TS_2 \tag{1.5}$$

Now it is a fundamental principle of thermodynamics that a system kept at constant pressure and temperature tends to a state of minimum free energy. Let $G_1 < G_2$; then at the temperature T the form of free energy G_1 is the more stable thermodynamically, and that of free energy G_2 should transform to it provided that there is a possible mechanism for the change (see next section); energy must be given out during the

13

process. Expressed otherwise, complete transformation to the alternative form should occur if $\Delta G < 0$, where ΔG is given by

$$\Delta G = \Delta H - T\Delta S \qquad (1.6)$$

and $$\Delta G = G_1 - G_2 = (H_1 - H_2) - T(S_1 - S_2)$$

(i.e. subtraction of eqn. 1.5 from eqn. 1.4).

At a triple point at which two allotropic forms are in equilibrium with the vapour of the element, e.g. point B in Fig. 1.2, the two forms must have the same free energy, i.e. $\Delta G = 0$ and hence (from eqn. 1.6) $\Delta H = T\Delta S$. (If the two forms were not of equal free energy, the system could reach a state of lower energy by transformation from one form to the other. Also, if two forms exist together under the same conditions, and have different free energies, the system is not at equilibrium, and the form of higher energy must be metastable with respect to that of lower energy.)

Since this discussion relates to allotropic changes during which not only the temperature but also the pressure is constant, and the change in volume is relatively small compared with the total volume of the system (i.e. the densities of the two forms are similar), the change in the term PV (eqn. 1.1) can be neglected so that $\Delta H \approx \Delta U$. ΔG then becomes approximately equal to the Helmholtz free energy change ΔF, defined by the equation,

$$\Delta F = \Delta U - \Delta S \qquad (1.7)$$

In order to appreciate how the stabilities of different allotropic forms vary with temperature, it is appropriate to consider first the change from rhombic to monoclinic sulphur. As noted on p. 11, the observed transition temperature is $95.5°C = 368.5°$ K, and the latent heat of transition is 2.81 cal/g $= 90.1$ cal/g-atom. The heat capacities at constant pressure of the two forms can be expressed by the following equations:

$$C_p \text{ (rhombic)} = 3.58 + 0.00624T$$

$$C_p \text{ (monoclinic)} = 3.56 + 0.00696T$$

It follows from eqn. (1.3) that the intergration of these equations with respect to temperature affords an expression for the heat contents of the two forms. It is more useful to consider the difference in the energies, etc., of the two forms (eqn. 1.6) than the absolute values of each (eqn. 1.1), and the difference in the heat contents of the two forms is given by:

$$\Delta H = \Delta H_0 - 0.02T + 0.00036T^2 \qquad (1.8)$$

where ΔH_0 (the difference between the integration constants) is the difference in the heat contents of the two forms at $0°$ K.

Since ΔH is known to be 90.1 cal/g-atom at $368.5°$ K, the substitution of these values into eqn. (1.8) allows the evaluation of ΔH_0 as 48.6 cal/g-atom. Hence, the difference in heat content at other temperatures is given by the equation:

$$\Delta H = 48.6 - 0.02\,T + 0.00036\,T^2 \qquad (1.9)$$

The variation of ΔG with temperature can also be obtained in a simple manner. Dividing throughout eqn. (1.6) by T gives,

$$\frac{\Delta G}{T} = \frac{\Delta H}{T} - \Delta S$$

and differentiating both sides with respect to T, gives,

$$\left(\frac{\partial(\Delta G/T)}{\partial T}\right)_P = -\frac{\Delta H}{T^2} \qquad (1.10)$$

Substituting the right-hand side of eqn. (1.9) for ΔH in this expression and integrating, gives

$$\frac{\Delta G}{T} = 48.6\,T^{-1} + 0.02\log_e T - 0.00036\,T + \text{const.}$$

Since $\Delta G = 0$ at $95.5°$ C ($368.5°$ K), substituting in the above equation allows the evaluation of the integration constant, and the following expression for the change in Gibbs free energy is obtained:

$$\Delta G = 48.6 + 0.02\,T\log_e T - 0.00036\,T^2 - 0.117\,T \qquad (1.11)$$

In Fig. 1.5 (*c*) the values of ΔG and ΔH evaluated from equations (1.11) and (1.9) are plotted against temperature over the range $0°$–$110°$C; the value of $T\Delta S$ (eqn. 1.6) is also shown.

Thus, the values both of ΔH and of $T\Delta S$ increase with increase in temperature. At low temperatures $\Delta H > T\Delta S$, so that ΔG is positive and the rhombic form is thermodynamically stable. The difference between the values of ΔH and of $T\Delta S$, and hence the value of ΔG also, decrease gradually until at the transition temperature $\Delta H = T\Delta S$ and $\Delta G = 0$, so that both forms are of equal stability. Above the transition temperature $T\Delta S > \Delta H$ and ΔG is negative so that the transition from the rhombic to the monoclinic form must take place at such temperatures.

The features of the discussion of this enantiotropic change apply equally to other systems. In Fig. 1.3 are shown the variation with temperature of the internal energies, entropies and free energies for two enantiotropic species of any element. The transition temperature, T_t, is the point at which $T\Delta S = \Delta U$. Two points should be noted before the main argument is presented. First, the variation in the internal energy,

15

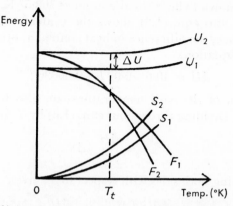

Fɪɢ. 1.3. Variation of internal energy (U), free energy (F) and entropy (S) for two allotropic forms, plotted against temperature. The transition temperature is shown by T_t.

U, with temperature is less than that of the heat content, H, since the change in volume is neglected. The heat content of sulphur was considered rather than the internal energy, since it is more readily obtained experimentally. Secondly, it follows from eqn. (1.6) that

$$\varDelta S = 1/T(\varDelta H - \varDelta G);$$

$\varDelta H$ is usually greater in magnitude than $\varDelta G$, at the corresponding temperature; accordingly, the sign of $\varDelta S$ is the same as that of $\varDelta H$, i.e. the form of higher heat content, and internal energy, is the form of higher entropy.

The form of lower internal energy, U_1, is stable below T_t, at which temperature $T\varDelta S = \varDelta U$ and $\varDelta G(\approx \varDelta F) = 0$. Above the transformation temperature the form of higher internal energy, U_2, is stable. At the

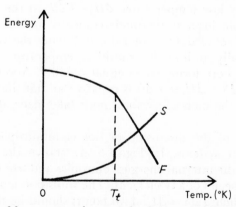

Fɪɢ. 1.4. Variation of free energy and entropy for the more stable allotropic form plotted against temperature. Compare with Fig. 1.3 which is on the same scale.

16

transformation temperature the energy ΔU must be supplied to allow the transition to occur, and this difference in internal energy is the latent heat of transformation.

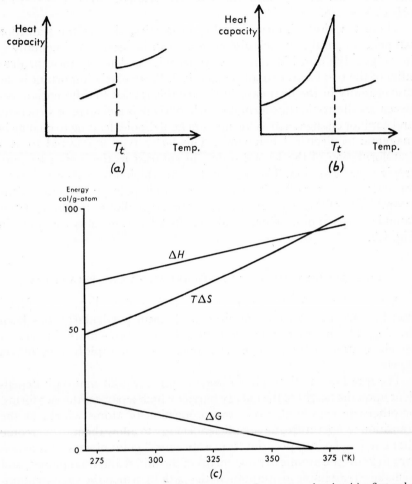

FIG. 1.5. Variation of heat capacity against temperature for a system showing (*a*) a first-order transformation and (*b*) a second-order transformation. (*c*) Variation of thermodynamic quantities for the change from rhombic to monoclinic sulphur.

When the resultant plot of F against T for the system of an element which is able to exist in two different forms, is drawn as in Fig. 1.3, it is seen to have a discontinuity at T_t, the transition temperature. Below T_t the plot follows that shown for F_1, and above T_t that shown for F_2 since the resultant must indicate the energy of the more stable form. Similarly the plot of S, for the more stable form, against T shows a discontinuity

17

corresponding to S_1 below T_t and S_2 at higher temperatures. These discontinuities are shown in Fig. 1.4, which is drawn to the same scale as Fig. 1.3. If the plot of either S or F against T shows a discontinuity, so also must the other, since the two are related. Since $F = U - TS$, $(\partial F / \partial T)_P = -S$.

There are discontinuities in other properties, also, at the transition temperature, and any such discontinuity can be used experimentally to investigate the transition. Such a property is the density, since the densities of the two forms cannot be identical. Particularly important is the discontinuity in the heat capacity, since this is used to differentiate between an allotropic transformation where there is a change in structure, and a minor change such as the alignment of dipoles leading to change in magnetic or electrical behaviour. This latter type is referred to as a transformation of the second order, in contrast to the first-order allotropic transformation. The temperature at which a second-order transformation occurs is often known as the lambda point, on account of the resemblance of the heat capacity v. temperature plot to the Greek letter lambda. Typical plots of first- and second-order transitions are shown in Fig. 1.5.

THE MECHANISM OF ALLOTROPIC TRANSFORMATIONS

A particularly useful approach to the structural implications of phase transformations, which emphasizes mechanism particularly, has been developed by Buerger. The arguments of this approach are directed at an elucidation of why some transitions proceed rapidly and others slowly.

The speed of an allotropic, or polymorphic, transformation is dependent upon the height of the energy barrier which separates the two forms, or otherwise expressed, upon the proportion of atoms which, at the transition temperature, have sufficient energy to allow them to overcome that barrier. To interpret this from a structural point of view, it is necessary to know the atomic arrangements of the initial and final phases, and to make a reasonable assumption of the path by which the various atoms must move during the transition.

The transition from one form to another is a change from a structure of one internal energy to that of another, while the intermediate state can possess an energy higher than those of the initial and final states. The internal energy of a material is a function of the particular arrangement of the atoms in the crystal lattice, i.e. of chemical bonding. The greater the number of bonds formed by each atom and the closer the atoms approach each other, the lower is the internal energy, since the greater amount of energy is given out during the formation of the lattice.

18

The form of an allotropic element which is stable at higher temperatures, and which has the higher internal energy, may thus be a form of lower coordination number, or greater interatomic distance, or may possibly possess a different type of chemical bonding. The less close approach of atoms can affect the immediate nearest neighbours of a given atom, or more distant atoms. These are referred to as changes in primary and secondary coordination respectively. In a molecular lattice, primary and secondary coordination represent intra- and inter-molecular distances respectively. Differences in bond type are illustrated by those elements one form of which shows metallic conductivity, whereas a second form behaves as an insulator. The nature of the bonding in such elements is discussed in a later section.

Buerger lists four classes of possible transformation, three of which are further subdivided, and suggests their relative rates. This classification is as follows:

(1) Transformations of secondary coordination:
    (*a*) Displacive   Rapid
    (*b*) Reconstructive   Sluggish
(2) Transformations of disorder:
    (*a*) Rotational   Rapid
    (*b*) Substitutional   Sluggish
(3) Transformations of first coordination:
    (*a*) Dilatational   Rapid
    (*b*) Reconstructive   Sluggish
(4) Transformations of bond type: Usually sluggish

The second of these four classes does not apply to the elements but only to compounds. This class will not be considered further, but each of the remaining three is considered in turn.

Transformations of secondary coordination are obviously less drastic from a structural standpoint than those which involve a change in the primary coordination of an atom, i.e. the nearest neighbours. Such a transformation is shown in Fig. 1.6 which represents a hypothetical two-dimensional network for a binary compound AB_2, where the coordination of atom A is four, and that of atom B is two. The structures shown as (*b*) and (*c*) in the Figure illustrate two forms which can transform into one another by a displacive transformation, i.e. one in which the atoms are only slightly displaced with respect to each other, and no bonds are broken. It can be seen that during such a transition each atom retains 'contact' with its immediate neighbours, although the change from (*c*) to (*b*) causes distortion and alters the arrangement of next-nearest neighbours, etc. The two forms must differ in their internal energy, therefore. There is no energy barrier of an intermediate structure

19

to make the transition difficult, so that the process should be rapid and be controlled only by the time required for the heat energy to travel through the lattice, i.e. the heat of transformation.

In the condensed form (*b*) it can be seen that atoms in secondary coordination approach more closely so that there is a stronger interaction, and hence this form is of lower internal energy than (*c*) and is the stable form at lower temperatures. Consider the effect of an input of heat into form (*b*); the atoms acquire thermal energy and in consequence vibrate

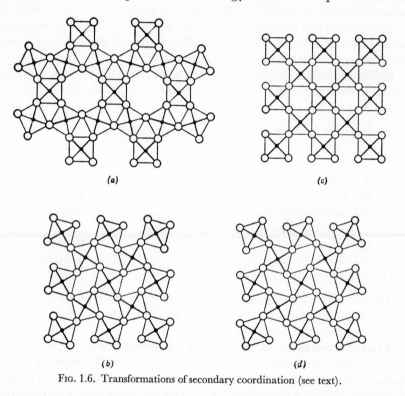

(*a*)

(*c*)

(*b*)

(*d*)

Fig. 1.6. Transformations of secondary coordination (see text).

about their lattice sites. When they have gained sufficient energy their vibrations cause them to take up the positions of the more open form (*c*), but as this represents a less favourable arrangement, the atoms can continue to move and take up the positions of structure (*d*)—a process which can be compared with an umbrella turning outside in. Now (*b*) and (*d*) are exactly equivalent, and with sufficient thermal energy to vibrate through the intermediate position (*c*) can change from one into the other. If this change occurs rapidly, then on a time average the structure is represented by (*c*), which can thus be considered as the high temperature stable modification. This displacement of atoms which produces a transformation from one form to another is thus an example of a *displacive transition.*

It is an important feature of this transition that the form which is stable at high temperature is the more open in structure. Accordingly, it has the higher entropy, the higher specific volume (lower density), and is likely to have a higher heat capacity since the atoms are further apart and less strongly bonded together, so that they can vibrate more easily and hence might be expected to absorb thermal energy more easily. The other important feature was stated above and can be emphasized again, i.e. since there is no energy barrier to overcome, the transition should be rapid and should take place as soon as the atoms have the necessary thermal energy.

In contrast to the mechanism of displacive transformation, that of a reconstructive transformation, as the term suggests, is a more drastic process. A reconstructive transformation of secondary coordination leaves the first coordination unchanged and alters only the secondary coordination, but with the important difference from a displacive transformation that bonds must be broken during the process. These bonds can even be bonds to first coordination atoms, but if these are broken new bonds must be formed before the stable final product is obtained.

An example of such a reconstructive transformation is the change from (*c*) to (*a*) in Fig. 1.6. Form (*a*) still retains the essential feature of 4:2 coordination shown by (*b*), (*c*) and (*d*), but change in secondary coordination has occurred. This change could not take place without the scission of bonds and the establishment of new bonds, in contrast to the displacive transformation considered above. The rupture of bonds entails a high energy barrier which has to be overcome during the transformation. Changes of this type, therefore, will be very sluggish when compared with displacive transformations which also modify the secondary coordination.

It is informative to consider the possible behaviour of two forms separated by such a reconstructive transformation, as the temperature is varied. Let A be the form of lower internal energy and B that of higher energy. If A is heated from normal temperature, the temperature T_t is reached at which both forms have the same free energy, and hence can exist together in equilibrium. Since the transformation is sluggish, i.e. has a high energy barrier it may however require an appreciable period of time for equilibrium to be established. If the temperature is raised above T_t, the formation of B can occur more rapidly since the atoms have additional thermal energy to assist them to overcome the energy barrier.

If B, once formed at this elevated temperature, is cooled slowly it can pass into the low temperature form A at T_t, but it is unlikely that the

21

transition can occur more easily in this direction than in the other. Accordingly an appreciable time must be allowed for the transformation to be complete, even at T_t. If, however, the temperature falls below T_t, the rate of transformation becomes slower and the time for complete transformation greater. If normal temperature is sufficiently far below T_t the rate of transformation becomes infinitely slow, and virtually undetectable. Now, if B had been cooled from the high temperature at which it is stable to normal temperature so rapidly that insufficient time was available for the transformation to A to occur, then B can be obtained at normal temperature at which it is not the thermodynamically stable form. The rate at which it can transform to the stable form A depends upon the height of the energy barrier, or less precisely the magnitude of the temperature difference between T_t and room temperature. (Even at T_t reconstructive transformation is slow in both directions, and the further the temperature below this, the slower the reaction will be in either direction.)

When B is obtained at any temperature below T_t, it is said to be metastable (as is A above T_t). Some metastable forms can be maintained at normal temperature for a very long period of time, if the energy barrier is sufficiently high. The best known example (though the transformation is not one of secondary coordination only) is diamond, and white phosphorus is another whose transformation is very slow. If the metastable form B is heated, the thermal energy acquired allows transformation to the stable form A at temperatures below T_t.

Three points supplementary to this discussion should be noted. First, a metastable form can sometimes be obtained by some sterically favourable mechanism, e.g. S_6 (p. 109), and can be monotropic instead of enantiotropic. Secondly, provided that it is thermodynamically favourable, a transformation can be accelerated by mechanical energy, as an alternative to thermal energy. Thirdly, a reconstructive transformation which might produce a form of lower internal energy but which has a transition temperature, T_t, below normal temperatures, would be expected to be very slow indeed, and perhaps undetectable, unless mechanical energy is supplied, e.g. the work of Barrett on low temperature forms of lithium and sodium (see pp. 71–72).

In the absence of any outside influence, a reconstructive transformation must involve a slow wave of transformation moving through the crystal lattice. The transformation can take place more readily if the substance has an appreciable vapour pressure at the appropriate temperature. A distillative mechanism is then possible, so that the less stable form more readily volatizes into the vapour phase, and condensation from the vapour to the solid takes place on nuclei of the more stable form, which thus grows continuously until the transition is complete. An alternative, and very similar process, can occur in the presence of a solvent, since the less stable form is the more soluble, and hence dissolves and crystallizes out as the more stable form.

Transformations of first coordination cause more profound change in the internal energy of the system, since this energy is very largely determined by the attractive forces of the nearest neighbours. Transformations of first coordination are less frequently encountered than those of secondary coordination. The transition from a body-centred cubic to a face-centred cubic structure is a dilatational transformation of first coordination, and is shown by some metals. This change alters the coordination of an atom from eight to twelve, and is considered from a structural point of view on p. 60. It involves an elongation, or dilatation, of the body-centred unit cell in one direction. It can be compared with the displacive transformation of secondary coordination, discussed above, in that no obvious energy barrier separates the two forms, and hence it should proceed rapidly when the appropriate temperature is reached.

Since the structure of lower coordination in such transitions is the more open structure, it is reasonable to expect that it should have the higher entropy and higher heat capacity; also, since a constituent atom has fewer immediate nearest neighbours, there is weaker bonding, and such a form should have higher internal energy. Hence for metals which show this particular transition from face-centred to body-centred cubic, the form of lower coordination, i.e. the body-centred, should be the high temperature form and the transition by which it is formed should proceed at an appropriate elevated temperature.

A reconstructional transformation of primary coordination is likely to proceed through an intermediate stage in which the coordination is other than that of the initial or final form, in contrast to a dilatational transformation of first coordination. The transformation requires a breaking of bonds and the formation of new bonds, and the intermediate phase represents an energy barrier, so that a direct parallel can be drawn to the reconstructive transformation of secondary coordination; such a transformation should thus take place more slowly than a dilatational transformation.

Transformations which involve change in bond type are rather more subtle, and can not be described on a simple structural basis alone, since electronic behaviour must also be taken into account. Tin undergoes such a transition very slowly, whereas selenium undergoes a very rapid transition of this type.

From the preceding discussion, it can be seen that a consideration of the mechanism of a transformation from a structural point of view affords a reasonable interpretation of relative rates of transformation.

23

Factors other than structure, and in particular particle size, can also affect the rate of a given transformation. Chemical reaction is frequently accelerated by diminution in particle size, since this increases surface area and allows a maximum possible contact between reactants. If a transformation proceeds by a solution mechanism, as outlined above, it should behave like a typical chemical reaction and be accelerated by decrease in particle size. In contrast, many transformations do not involve contact with a solvent and require a nucleus or centre for their initiation. It follows that the larger the number of particles the larger is the number of nuclei which is required, and the more difficult it will be to transfer heat energy from one particle to another, i.e. through the mass, on account of the air cushion between the particles. Accordingly many transformations of this kind take place most rapidly in single crystals.

The emphasis throughout the preceding section has been on transformations brought about by change in temperature. It should be re-emphasized that transformations can be brought about by the use of mechanical energy also, e.g. by scratching or rubbing a material, and by the well-known 'cold-working' of metals. In such cases the mechanical and not the thermal energy allows the atoms to overcome the energy barrier.

Reference should also be made to the extensive researches of Bridgman who has studied the behaviour of many materials under pressures up to 10^5 atmospheres. These researches not only allow the study of known fusion and transition curves to very high pressures, but also led to the detection of hitherto unknown transitions of a number of elements, by measured discontinuities in physical properties. The experimental conditions made it impossible to determine the crystal structure of these new modifications, and for this reason they are not discussed in this account. An interested reader will find a review with numerous references to this work in *Reviews of Modern Physics*, 1946, **18**, 1.

MARTENSITIC TRANSFORMATIONS

The discussion of thermodynamics and mechanism which has been given above applies to transformations between structures which are covalently bonded (i.e. non-metals), and to certain metal transformations. There are however a number of transformations from one metal lattice to another which have characteristics of behaviour different from those described above. These are known after the transformation which yields martensite, a form of iron containing a small proportion of carbon. Martensitic transformations are encountered in a number of alloy systems, and in a number of pure metals also, although not every transition from one metal lattice to another is martensitic.

24

Perhaps the most characteristic feature of these transformations is that they do not go to completion at a given temperature and are not reversible in a strictly thermodynamic sense, although they are structurally reversible. Thus, if a high temperature form is cooled down to the temperature, T', at which the low temperature form has the same free energy, and is maintained at that temperature, no change to the low temperature form occurs. The metal must be cooled further to a temperature denoted as M_s (start of martensitic phase) before any of the low temperature form appears. If cooling is stopped at that point, no further change occurs, but if the temperature is lowered by a further increment, more of the low temperature form is produced. Eventually a temperature, T'', is reached which is appreciably below both T' and M_s, at which the transformation is complete. The transformation can be reversed to give the high temperature form, although the temperature range need not coincide exactly with that observed on cooling. It is impossible to cool the high temperature form to low temperatures sufficiently rapidly to preserve it in a metastable condition.

Martensitic transformations are sometimes known as diffusionless, which indicates the other most important feature, that they involve the shear of one or more planes of atoms, through relatively short distances, i.e. less than an interatomic distance. During such a shear the planes must adhere together perfectly. A transition does not cover the entire crystal at one time, but involves small parts of the crystal in turn. This results in the formation of small plates, and these can be observed as surface irregularities in the crystal of the transformation product. Microscopic recognition of such irregularities is an important means of determining that such a transformation has occurred. It is not always known with certainty whether a given metallic transformation is martensitic or not, nor, if it is martensitic, which are the precise directions of shear. Such studies are not easy, and understandably the metallurgists, within whose sphere of research they fall, have obtained more data on transformations in alloy systems which are of constructional use, than on those of pure metals which are not. The structural aspects of martensitic transformations will be considered in a later section (p. 59 *et seq.*) but the thermodynamic behaviour can be considered appropriately at this point.

Since equilibrium between the two forms is not established at T' at which the free energies of the two are equal, i.e. $\Delta F = 0$, there must be a further energy term to take into account. When the metal is cooled (this is the direction in which transformations are usually studied, since the product is stable at low temperatures and is amenable to microscopic study, etc., whereas the high temperature form obtained on heating is not), the thermal energy corresponding to the difference in temperature $T' - M_s$ must be a critical amount of energy, so that when M_s is reached transformation can start. The condition for the appearance of the low temperature phase can be written as:

$$\Delta F + \Delta F' = 0$$

where $\Delta F'$ is the term to be interpreted. It must increase in magnitude as the transformation proceeds, otherwise complete formation of the low temperature form would occur at M_s. It is believed that the term represents a strain energy associated with the formation of new surfaces during the transformation. No such strain energy arises in those transformations which proceed without the shear of planes of atoms, hence these can occur when $\Delta F = 0$, whereas martensitic transformations occur over a range of temperature.

CHAPTER 2

CHEMICAL BONDING IN THE ELEMENTS

When two atoms approach each other closely, both an attractive force and a repulsive force are exerted between them as a consequence of the electrical charges associated with their constituent protons and electrons. These forces are inversely proportional to different powers of the interatomic separation, and this is shown diagrammatically in Fig. 2.1 for a hypothetical case. It can be seen that the force of repulsion increases

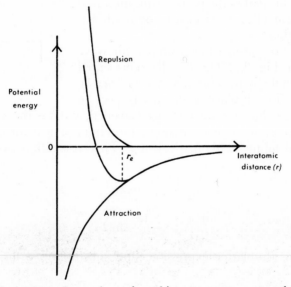

Fig. 2.1. The resultant of attraction and repulsion as two atoms approach each other.

particularly rapidly when the nuclei approach very closely, since this approach causes interpenetration of the negatively charged electronic shells. The resultant obtained by the addition of the forces of repulsion and attraction passes through a minimum of energy at a particular distance. This is the equilibrium distance at which the atoms will come to rest.

The precise way in which these forces vary with the interatomic separation depends upon the nature of the chemical bond formed between the atoms, and the deeper the minimum of energy the more

27

strongly are the atoms held together. As the attractive force which holds the atoms together depends upon the exact nature of the outermost parts of the two atoms, viz. their electronic arrangements, an approach to chemical bonding must start with an electronic theory of the atom.

ELECTRONIC THEORY OF THE ATOM

Bohr's theory made an important step towards an understanding of the behaviour of electrons since it afforded an interpretation of the known spectrum of the hydrogen atom. Each line of this spectrum corresponds to an electronic transition between two different fixed energy levels, or states, and Bohr was able to calculate the differences in energy between these levels, and hence the wavelengths of the observed spectral lines. A more complete understanding of electronic behaviour became possible when the science of wave mechanics was applied to the problem. This makes the basic assumption that the behaviour of an electron can be treated as a wave motion.

It is useful to consider first a simple sine wave as shown in Fig. 2.2. This can be represented mathematically by the equation $\psi = \sin 2\pi(x/\lambda)$, where ψ is the displacement with respect to

FIG. 2.2. A sine wave, $\psi = \sin 2\pi(x/\lambda)$.

zero for any value of x, the distance travelled, and λ is the wavelength.

This equation is not in a very useful form but can be made more useful after several simple mathematical steps. First, it is differentiated twice, giving successively:

$$\frac{d\psi}{dx} = \frac{2\pi}{\lambda}\cos 2\pi\frac{x}{\lambda}$$

and

$$\frac{d^2\psi}{dx^2} = -\frac{4\pi^2}{\lambda^2}\sin 2\pi\frac{x}{\lambda}$$

Rearranging this latter expression, and substituting ψ for $\sin 2\pi(x/\lambda)$ gives:

$$\frac{d^2\psi}{dx^2} + \frac{4\pi^2}{\lambda^2}\psi = 0 \qquad (2.1)$$

One obvious solution to this equation is $\psi = \sin 2\pi(x/\lambda)$, which is of course a wave function.

An energy term is now introduced into the equation by using the well-known relationship, $\lambda = h/mv$, where h is Planck's constant, and m and v are the mass and velocity of the particle whose behaviour is described by the wave of length λ. The expression then becomes:

$$\frac{d^2\psi}{dx^2} + \frac{4\pi^2 m^2 v^2}{h^2}\psi = 0$$

Finally, the undesired term v, the velocity, is eliminated by using the relationship:

$$\text{Kinetic Energy} = \text{Total Energy} - \text{Potential Energy}$$

i.e. $\quad\quad\quad\quad\quad \tfrac{1}{2}mv^2 = E - V$

or $\quad\quad\quad\quad\quad\quad v^2 = \dfrac{2(E - V)}{m}$

and, substituting, the expression becomes:

$$\frac{\mathrm{d}^2\psi}{\mathrm{d}x^2} + \frac{8\pi^2 m}{h^2}(E - V)\psi = 0 \quad\quad\quad (2.2)$$

This equation, when solved for ψ, gives information about the behaviour in space and the energy of a particle of mass m travelling in one dimension with a motion which can be described by a sine wave. When an electron is considered to have wave characteristics, the appropriate mathematical treatment must apply to three dimensions instead of one, so that it involves the coordinates x, y and z. The equation proposed by Schrodinger to describe the behaviour of an electron is therefore:

$$\frac{\partial^2\psi}{\partial x^2} + \frac{\partial^2\psi}{\partial y^2} + \frac{\partial^2\psi}{\partial z^2} + \frac{8\pi^2 m}{h^2}(E - V)\psi = 0$$

or $\quad\quad\quad\quad \nabla^2\psi + \dfrac{8\pi^2 m}{h^2}(E - V)\psi = 0 \quad\quad\quad (2.3)$

where ψ represents a displacement function,

$\quad\quad x, y$ and z are the normal Cartesian coordinates,

$\quad\quad m$ is the mass of the electron,

$\quad\quad h$ is Planck's constant,

$\quad\quad E$ is the total energy of the electron,

$\quad\quad V$ is the potential energy of the electron.

It can be seen that eqn. (2.3) has features in common with the one-dimensional eqn. (2.2); ψ is now, however, a function of x, y and z. The solutions of this equation for ψ afford the necessary information about the behaviour of individual electrons. It is possible to solve the equation rigorously only for hydrogen-like atoms, i.e. where a single electron is under the influence of a point positive charge, since the potential energy term, V, can not be evaluated accurately for multi-electron atoms and approximations must be made.

Acceptable solutions of eqn. (2.3) for ψ are possible only for certain definite values of E. That is to say, each electron possesses a definite

29

amount of energy, or exists in a state of definite energy. An electron can acquire additional energy from an external source, but only if the amount of this energy corresponds with the difference between its existing state and another state which also corresponds with a solution of the wave equation. The magnitudes of the energy involved in such transitions are obtained experimentally by a study of atomic absorption spectra.

It is beyond the scope of this text to indicate the procedure required for the solution of the wave equation, but some features of the process must be mentioned since they are of chemical significance. First, it is

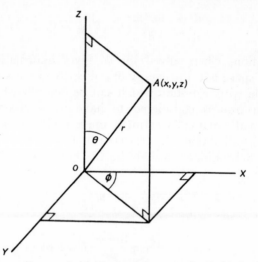

FIG. 2.3. The polar coordinates r, θ and ϕ for the electron at point A with Cartesian coordinates x, y and z are as shown. It can be calculated that the following relationships are true: $x = r\sin\theta\cos\phi$, $y = r\sin\theta\sin\phi$ and $z = r\cos\theta$.

advantageous to change from Cartesian to polar coordinates, i.e. from x, y and z to r, θ and ϕ. The relationship between the two is illustrated in Fig. 2.3.

Each solution of the wave equation can be written as the product of three functions, i.e.

$$\psi = f(r) . f'(\theta) . f''(\phi)$$

where the first function varies only with distance (r), and the remaining two only with angle or direction (θ and ϕ). Furthermore, the solutions involve quantities which must, of mathematical necessity, be integral. (These integers arise from the need to obtain the sum of an infinite series to a finite number of terms.) These integers are known as quantum numbers and each solution to the wave equation is characterized by a different set of three quantum numbers. These are known as the principal

30

(n), the secondary or azimuthal (l) and the magnetic (m) quantum numbers, and they can have values defined by the following conditions:

$$n = 1, 2, 3, 4, \ldots n$$
$$l = (n-1), (n-2), (n-3) \ldots 0$$
$$m = l, (l-1), (l-2), \ldots 0 \ldots -(l-2), -(l-1), -l$$

In Table 2.1 the possible combinations of these quantum numbers are shown for values of $n = 1$, 2 and 3; the extension to higher values of n is a simple exercise. It is important to be familiar with the shorthand designation of each of these combinations of quantum numbers, i.e. solutions to the wave equation, which will be referred to subsequently as *orbitals*.

Table 2.1.

n	l	m	Designation	
1	0	0	1s	Note that in each designation the
2	0	0	2s	number is that of the principal
2	1	1 ⎫		quantum number, n, and the
2	1	0 ⎬	2p	letter represents the secondary
2	1	−1 ⎭		quantum number, l; thus,
3	0	0	3s	s corresponds to $l = 0$
3	1	1 ⎫		p „ „ $l = 1$
3	1	0 ⎬	3p	d „ „ $l = 2$
3	1	−1 ⎭		f „ „ $l = 3$
3	2	2 ⎫		
3	2	1 ⎪		
3	2	0 ⎬	3d	
3	2	−1 ⎪		
3	2	−2 ⎭		

It was noted above that each orbital is a product of functions of r, θ and ϕ. To obtain a pictorial representation of each orbital, it is necessary to consider separately the radial function $f(r)$, which is completely independent of direction, and the combined angular function $f(\theta, \phi)$, which is similarly completely independent of distance. The radial function varies with the values of n and l, whereas the angular function varies with the values of l and m, and is independent of that of n. For the purposes of this book the radial functions need not be considered further. The angular functions, however, are very important and must be considered further. Fortunately these are the same whether the atom considered is hydrogen-like or not, so that it is possible to refer to s, p, d or f orbitals for all atoms in the same way.

Each orbital, as was pointed out above, corresponds to a definite energy and has definite calculable radial and angular properties. Two further points must also be noted. First, each orbital can describe two electrons, but only when these are of opposite 'spin'. To complete the

31

characterization of an electron a fourth quantum number, known as the spin quantum number, is introduced, and this can have a value of $+\frac{1}{2}$ or $-\frac{1}{2}$. Each electron is characterized by four quantum numbers, and it is not allowed that any two electrons of the same atom have the same

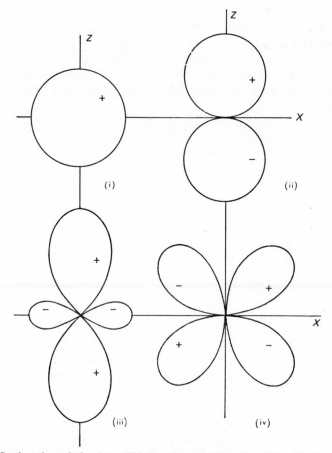

FIG. 2.4. Sections through the plots of $f(\theta, \phi)$ against θ and ϕ for (i) s, (ii) p_z, (iii) d_{z^2} and (iv) d_{zx} atomic orbitals (drawn to scale). The p_x and p_y orbitals resemble the p_z, and d_{xy} and $_{zx}$ resembled d_{zx}, with an appropriate change of axes in each case; the remaining $d_{x^2-y^2}$ orbital resembles the d_{zx} orbital but its maximum extensions coincide exactly with the x and y axes, instead of being at 45° to axes, as are the d_{zx}, d_{xy} and d_{yz} orbitals.

set of values for these quantum numbers. The two electrons of one orbital have identical values for three quantum numbers, but differ in the value of the spin quantum number.

Secondly, it is necessary to comment upon the significance of ψ. When the term was introduced it was said to be equivalent to the amplitude of a simple wave, but the three-dimensional interpretation of this is difficult. It is known that the intensity of a wave is proportional to the square of the amplitude; so also is the 'intensity' of the electron proportional to ψ^2. The intensity is the probability of finding the electron. Hence the square of the function $f(\theta,\phi)$ gives the probability of finding

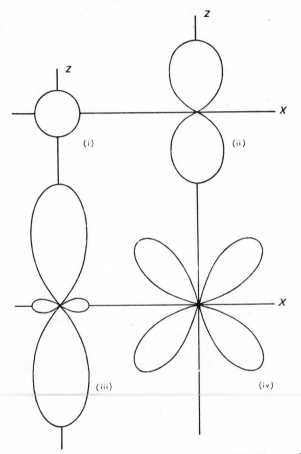

FIG. 2.5. Sections through the plots of $[f(\theta,\phi)]^2$ for the orbitals illustrated in Fig. 2.4.

the appropriate electron in directions corresponding to any values of θ and ϕ. It is not possible to pin-point either the position of an electron at a given instant of time, or to define accurately the path taken by an electron, but only to refer to the probability of finding it at a certain distance $[f(r)]^2$ or in a given direction $[f(\theta,\phi)]^2$.

In Figs 2.4 and 2.5 are shown plots of the angular function and angular probability against θ and ϕ for a number of atomic orbitals.

33

Probability is always positive, so that no signs appear in Fig. 2.5, but the positive and negative signs in the various lobes of Fig. 2.4 arise since the functions of θ and ϕ change sign according the values of these angles. The directional properties of the atomic orbitals are referred to again in the discussion of covalent bonding.

The relative energies of the various orbitals are of appreciable chemical significance, also, and these can be calculated theoretically or determined experimentally by a study of atomic spectra. When the sequence of energy levels is established electrons are fed into them so that the level of lowest energy is filled first, and thereafter levels are occupied in order of increasing energy. Following this procedure, it is possible to obtain the electronic configurations of all the elements. It should be borne in mind that those orbitals which are not occupied† when the atom is in its lowest, or ground state, are nevertheless available and can become occupied when an appropriate amount of energy is supplied to the atom. It is then said to be in an excited state.

THE PERIODIC TABLE

The sequence in which the various energy levels are occupied as the atomic number of the element increases is as follows: $1s$, $2s$, $2p$, $3s$, $3p$, $4s$, $3d$, $4p$, $5s$, $4d$, $5p$, $6s$, $4f$, $5d$, $6p$, $7s$, $6d \approx 5f$. This is the sequence of increase in the value of $(n + l)$; when two levels have the same value for $(n + l)$, that with the lower value of n has the lower energy.

The elements hydrogen, atomic number 1, and helium, atomic number 2, have one and two electrons respectively in the orbital of lowest energy, i.e. their configurations are written as $1s^1$ and $1s^2$. In lithium and beryllium, atomic numbers 3 and 4, the next level, $2s$, is occupied singly and doubly in addition to the $1s$, so that their configurations are written as $1s^2 2s^1$ and $1s^2 2s^2$. The continuance of this process makes it possible to write down the configuration of every element in its ground state. When the elements are then arranged in order of increasing atomic number so that those which have identical configurations in their outermost shell appear in vertical groups, the Periodic Table as shown in Fig. 2.6 is obtained.

It can be seen from Table 2.1 that there are three p orbitals and five d orbitals for each appropriate value of the principal quantum number; similarly there are seven f orbitals. In a free atom every orbital within any such group has the same energy, and orbitals of the same energy are said to be degenerate; such a degenerate group of orbitals can be

---

† An orbital was defined as a solution of the wave equation. The solution is a function of coordinates of space, and it is hence conventional to regard an orbital as space which can be occupied by electrons.

FIG. 2.6. PERIODIC TABLE OF THE ELEMENTS

				Groups					Inert gas electrons
1	2	3	4	5	6	7	0		

Period 1 **1s** $_1$H $_2$He   2

2 **2s** $_3$Li $_4$Be   **2p** $_5$B $_6$C $_7$N $_8$O $_9$F $_{10}$Ne   2,8

3 **3s** $_{11}$Na $_{12}$Mg   **3p** $_{13}$Al $_{14}$Si $_{15}$P $_{16}$S $_{17}$Cl $_{18}$Ar   2,8,8

4 **4s** $_{19}$K $_{20}$Ca **3d** $_{21}$Sc $_{22}$Ti $_{23}$V $_{24}$Cr $_{25}$Mn $_{26}$Fe $_{27}$Co $_{28}$Ni $_{29}$Cu $_{30}$Zn **4p** $_{31}$Ga $_{32}$Ge $_{33}$As $_{34}$Se $_{35}$Br $_{36}$Kr   2,8,18,8

5 **5s** $_{37}$Rb $_{38}$Sr **4d** $_{39}$Y $_{40}$Zr $_{41}$Nb $_{42}$Mo $_{43}$Tc $_{44}$Ru $_{45}$Rh $_{46}$Pd $_{47}$Ag $_{48}$Cd **5p** $_{49}$In $_{50}$Sn $_{51}$Sb $_{52}$Te $_{53}$I $_{54}$Xe   2,8,18,18,8

6 **6s** $_{55}$Cs $_{56}$Ba **5d** $_{57}$La $_{72}$Hf $_{73}$Ta $_{74}$W $_{75}$Re $_{76}$Os $_{77}$Ir $_{78}$Pt $_{79}$Au $_{80}$Hg **6p** $_{81}$Tl $_{82}$Pb $_{83}$Bi $_{84}$Po $_{85}$At $_{86}$Rn   2,8,18,32,18,8

7 **7s** $_{87}$Fr $_{88}$Ra **6d** $_{89}$Ac
etc.

Lanthanides **4f** $_{58}$Ce $_{59}$Pr $_{60}$Nd $_{61}$Pm $_{62}$Sm $_{63}$Eu $_{64}$Gd $_{65}$Tb $_{66}$Dy $_{67}$Ho $_{68}$Er $_{69}$Tm $_{70}$Yb $_{71}$Lu

Actinides **5f** $_{90}$Th $_{91}$Pa $_{92}$U $_{93}$Np $_{94}$Pu $_{95}$Am $_{96}$Cm $_{97}$Bk $_{98}$Cf $_{99}$Es $_{100}$Fm $_{101}$Md $_{102}$No $_{103}$Lw

35

referred to as an energy level. The manner in which such a set of orbitals of equal energy is filled is in accordance with Hund's rule, which states that in the ground state of the atom, electrons occupy a set of degenerate orbitals in such a way that as many as possible have the same value for the spin quantum number, i.e. their spins are parallel. Thus in the series of elements from boron to neon, which corresponds with the filling of the three degenerate $2p$ orbitals, boron, carbon and nitrogen have one, two and three orbitals singly occupied; oxygen is the first of the series which has a doubly occupied $2p$ orbital. Hund's rule applies equally to each set of p, d and f orbitals.

Two qualifications of the above discussion must be noted. First, in a hydrogen-like atom there is more extensive degeneracy since the $2s$ and $2p$ orbitals are of equal energy, as are the $3s$, $3p$ and $3d$, etc. Secondly, there are some minor irregularities in the pattern of electronic configurations. Thus, the group of elements nickel, palladium and platinum have the configurations d^8s^2, $d^{10}s^0$, and d^9s^1 respectively, which would not be predicted from simple considerations. There are other such examples, but these are seldom of chemical significance.

In the Periodic Table illustrated, the precise energy level which is being filled is indicated immediately before the first element in which it is occupied.

CHEMICAL BONDING

The electronic theory of the atom is a stepping stone towards a theory of the combination of atoms. This is of course, more important for the purpose of this book, since few elements exist as free atoms in the uncombined state, particularly under normal conditions of temperature and pressure. Just as it was impossible to make precise calculations of the energy, etc., of an electron for an atom with more than one electron so it is impossible also for systems containing more than one atom.

(i) Diatomic Molecules. A system of two atoms only will be considered first, and the hydrogen molecule which has only two electrons is the simplest example. The behaviour of any one electron can no longer be described by a function which relates to only one nucleus; each electron is considered to be in a molecular orbital, instead of an atomic orbital, and the function which describes it has something of the character of the individual atomic orbitals of the constituent atoms.

Let the atoms of the molecule be referred to as A and B, and let the corresponding electrons be described by the wave functions ψ_A and ψ_B when the two atoms are infinitely far apart. It is assumed in the conventional molecular orbital treatment that the solutions to the wave equation which describe the diatomic (bicentric) system are $a\psi_A \pm a\psi_B$, where a is a constant. (If the atoms are of different elements two different constants are required.) Thus, two atomic orbitals, one of atom A and one of atom B, have been 'compounded' to form the same number of molecular orbitals, each of which has something of the character of the parent atomic orbitals, since the functions which described the atomic orbitals are both included in the functions which describe the molecular orbitals. Each electron is influenced by both nuclei instead of by one only as in the isolated atom.

Just as the energies and directional properties of atomic orbitals can be calculated, so also can those of molecular orbitals, and the results are of considerable importance. The relative energies of the two molecular orbitals compared with the energy of the atomic orbitals of the isolated atoms are shown in Fig. 2.7. One molecular orbital corresponds to a lower energy than that of the atomic orbitals, whereas the other corresponds to a higher energy, the downward displacement on the energy

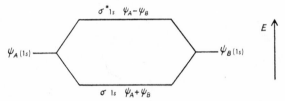

FIG. 2.7. The combination of the $1s$ atomic orbitals of atoms A and B to form σ (bonding) and σ^* (antibonding) molecular orbitals.

scale being exactly equal to the upward displacement. Since the two molecular orbitals are not degenerate, the two electrons occupy the orbital of lower energy, which results in a net stabilization of the system compared with that of two isolated atoms. The orbital which contains the two electrons is called a bonding orbital, and the vacant orbital of higher energy is an antibonding orbital. A study of the spectrum of molecular hydrogen shows that the transition of an electron from the bonding to the anti-bonding orbital requires an energy of 250 kcal/mole.

Just as the hydrogen atomic orbitals which are occupied in the free atom, i.e. the $1s$ orbitals, can combine to form two molecular orbitals denoted $\sigma 1s$ and $\sigma^* 1s$, so also can the higher atomic orbitals which are normally unoccupied in the free atom. These molecular orbitals are also vacant in the ground state of the hydrogen molecule, but can be occupied if the appropriate excitation energy is supplied to the molecule. Thus there is a parallel with atomic orbitals and atomic spectra, and this parallel can be taken further since these molecular orbitals of higher energy derived from atomic orbitals of higher energy are occupied in

37

molecules of elements of atomic number greater than that of hydrogen; these will be discussed below.

It is necessary to discuss the electronic distribution in the various possible molecular orbitals. One way to represent this is shown in Fig. 2.8 for the combination of atomic $1s$ orbitals. The angular distribution functions for the free atoms are allowed to approach so closely that some overlap occurs. The molecular orbital representation is obtained by drawing and adding the vectors from the mid-point of the two nuclei to the circumference of the two atomic orbitals for every possible angle. It can be seen that for the bonding orbital the electron density is increased between the two nuclei, whereas in the antibonding orbital this is not so.

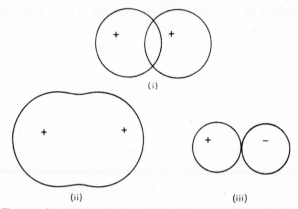

FIG. 2.8. (i) Two overlapping atomic $1s$ orbitals; (ii) the bonding molecular orbital, and (iii) the antibonding molecular orbital derived from them vectorially.

This picture of the bonding molecular orbital corresponds closely with the familiar picture of an electron pair holding two nuclei together. It can be imagined that the negative charge placed between the two positively charged nuclei prevents these from recoiling apart because of the repulsion of like charges. In contrast the antibonding orbital has no such beneficial concentration of negative charge.

The molecular orbitals derived from p atomic orbitals by the same procedure are shown in Fig. 2.9. It can be seen that the molecular orbitals derived from p_x orbitals are similar to those from the s orbitals, since the bonding orbital results from an overlap of atomic orbitals along the line joining the two atomic nuclei. To indicate this symmetry of the overlap the prefix σ (sigma) is used to describe the molecular orbital. In contrast, the bonding molecular orbitals derived from the p_y and p_z atomic orbitals do not possess a region of overlap on the line joining the atomic nuclei; there are two regions of overlap one above and one below this line, and the symmetry of this overlap is denoted by the prefix π (pi).

38

(By convention, an asterisk denotes that the molecular orbital is anti-bonding.)

It is clear from the diagrams of Figs. 2.8 and 2.9 that the atomic orbitals can combine to form a bonding molecular orbital only if they

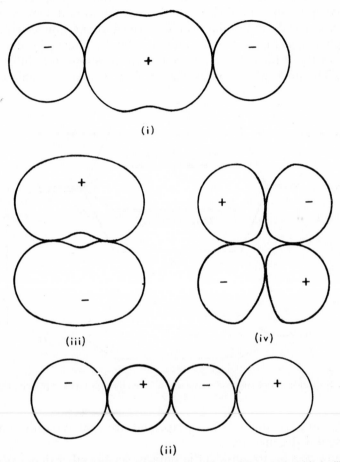

(i)

(iii)   (iv)

(ii)

FIG. 2.9. Molecular orbitals derived by combination of $2p_x$ and $2p_z$ atomic orbitals. (i) bonding $\sigma 2p_x$, (ii) antibonding $\sigma*2p_x$ (iii) bonding $\pi 2p_z$, and (iv) antibonding $\pi*2p_z$. The $\pi 2p_y$ and $\pi*2p_y$ are analogous with πp_z and $\pi*p_z$ with respect to the appropriate axis.

have the same sign in the regions where they overlap. It is also necessary that the atomic nuclei approach sufficiently closely to allow the overlap, and that the atomic orbitals should have very similar energy in the free atoms—a condition which is exactly realized when the atoms of an element combine, but not necessarily when atoms of two different elements combine to form a compound.

39

Before considering molecules other than hydrogen, it is necessary to establish the sequence of molecular orbitals in order of increasing energy content. This is illustrated in Fig. 2.10 for those derived from atomic orbitals of principal quantum number 2, and this Figure should be compared with Fig. 2.7, which shows the orbitals corresponding to the principal quantum number of 1. A most important feature of this sequence is that the molecular orbitals derived from p atomic orbitals are not triply degenerate as are the atomic orbitals. Thus the difference in the symmetry of the overlap referred to above results in a difference in energy. The molecular orbitals derived from p_y and p_z atomic orbitals

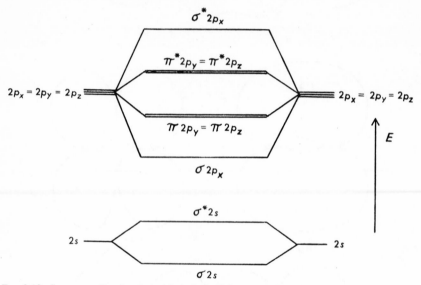

FIG. 2.10. Sequence of molecular orbitals derived from atomic orbitals of principal quantum number 2 (not to scale).

have the same symmetry of overlap, and are exactly equivalent and hence doubly degenerate.

It is now possible to consider diatomic molecules other than hydrogen. The procedure is to regard the two nuclei as a compound nucleus and to feed the total number of electrons that they possess into the molecular orbitals starting with that of lowest energy. Hund's rule must be applied again to the filling of degenerate orbitals. As has been seen from Figs. 2.7 and 2.10 the stabilization obtained by the occupancy of a bonding orbital is exactly equal to the destabilization which results from the occupancy of an antibonding orbital. Hence a diatomic molecule is stabilized with respect to the free atoms if the number of electrons in bonding orbitals exceeds the number in antibonding orbitals. The bond

40

order can be defined as the difference between the number of bonding and antibonding orbitals filled, i.e. doubly occupied, and the greater its value the greater the stabilization, the stronger the bond between the atoms, and the smaller the interatomic separation.

Descriptions of the electronic configurations of diatomic molecules for elements of atomic number 1–10 are given in Table 2.2. The exact balancing of bonding and antibonding contributions in helium, beryllium and neon, which results from the complete occupancy of an s or p orbital, should be noted. Such molecules are not stable. A diatomic molecule of lithium is closely analogous to that of hydrogen; stable diatomic molecules of boron and carbon should also be more stable than the free atoms but are of little importance except at very high temperatures. It is known, of course, that fluorine, oxygen and nitrogen exist as diatomic molecules under normal conditions, and hence these require further comment.

Table 2.2. Electronic Configurations of Diatonic Molecules of Elements of Atomic Number 1–10

Element	Atomic configuration	Molecular configuration	Bond order
H	$1s^1$	$(\sigma 1s)^2$	1
He	$1s^2$	$(\sigma 1s)^2 (\sigma^* 1s)^2$	0
Li	$2s^1$	$(\sigma 2s)^2$	1
Be	$2s^2$	$(\sigma 2s)^2 (\sigma^* 2s)^2$	0
B	$2s^2 2p^1$	$(\sigma 2p_x)^2$	1
C	$2s^2 2p^2$	$(\sigma 2p_x)^2 (\pi 2p_y)^1 (\pi 2p_z)^1$	2
N	$2s^2 2p^3$	$(\sigma 2p_x)^2 (\pi 2p_y = \pi 2p_z)^4$	3
O	$2s^2 2p^4$	$(\sigma 2p_x)^2 (\pi 2p_y = \pi 2p_z)^4 (\pi^* 2p_y)^1 (\pi^* 2p_z)^1$	2
F	$2s^2 2p^5$	$(\sigma 2p_x)^2 (\pi 2p_y = \pi 2p_z)^4 (\pi^* 2p_y = \pi^* 2p_z)^4$	1
Ne	$2s^2 2p^6$	$(\sigma 2p_x)^2 (\pi 2p_y = \pi 2p_z)^4 (\pi^* 2p_y = \pi^* 2p_z)^4 (\sigma^* 2p_x)^2$	0

Since the contributions to bonding and antibonding from a complete s level are equal, these have been omitted from the molecular configurations of the later elements for convenience.

In fluorine the contributions to bonding by the σs, πp_y and πp_z orbitals are exactly cancelled by the corresponding antibonding orbitals, and net bonding is due to the σp_x orbital (see Fig. 2.10). This is referred to as a single or sigma bond. In the nitrogen molecule, if the filled s levels are ignored, three bonding orbitals are occupied but no antibonding orbitals, so that the atoms are held together by three bonds—one sigma and two pi, and this is referred to commonly as a triple bond. The overlapping can be imagined by a consideration of Fig. 2.9. The molecule is much more stable with respect to its atoms than is the fluorine molecule, and the well known difference in chemical reactivity of the two elements is in accord with this.

41

The bonding in the oxygen molecule is intermediate between that in the molecules of nitrogen and fluorine. Three bonding orbitals are occupied and two antibonding orbitals half-occupied (this is because of the degeneracy), so that the net bond order is $3 - 2 \times \frac{1}{2} = 2$, i.e. a double bond. Since the molecule has two unpaired electrons, it shows paramagnetism.

The development of molecular orbitals which has been outlined above as a description of diatomic molecules, is straightforward and gives a good explanation of experimental observations. The majority of substances do not, however, exist as diatomic molecules, and the extension of these ideas to larger molecules is not always easy. In principle, the wave function for each molecular orbital consists of a series of as many terms as there are atoms in the molecule, and the molecule can be indefinitely large, e.g. a crystal of a metal, or diamond. Each term is the wave function for an atomic orbital with an appropriate coefficient, e.g. $\Psi_{MO} = a\psi_1 + b\psi_2 + c\psi_3 + d\psi_4 \ldots$, etc.

For the purpose of this book, no such complete description of molecular orbitals will be attempted. In many molecules it is convenient to regard an electron pair as localized between two atoms and to neglect the possibility that these electrons can be at any point within the molecule. Mathematically, this means that the wave function used for the molecular orbital consists of two terms only, as in diatomic molecules, and it is assumed that the coefficients of all the remaining terms are effectively zero, i.e. the electron is never described by the wave functions of atoms other than the two between which it is localized. The bonding of many forms of many elements can be described adequately by making this approximation of localized molecular orbitals.

The physical properties, particularly conductivity, of some other 'molecules' can be interpreted only if delocalized molecular orbitals which extend over all the atoms are assumed. This is applicable particularly to the metals. It will not be necessary to write down a wave function to describe such an orbital. The criterion for such a delocalized orbital is that all the constituent atoms possess atomic orbitals which have the correct symmetry to overlap with more than one neighbouring atom. Bonding in polyatomic systems is now described using these two approaches.

(ii) Polyatomic Molecules with Localized Orbitals. The formation of a bond between two atoms of an element requires that the atoms should have unpaired electrons in identical atomic orbitals, and also that these two orbitals should overlap as completely as possible. If, for example, a carbon atom of electronic configuration $s^2 p^2$ is considered, only the p electrons are unpaired, and two bonds should be formed per carbon atom, which disagrees with the observed value of four. Further, if a carbon atom uses p orbitals the greatest possible overlap will result if atoms approach it from directions which are at right angles to each other, since p orbitals are mutually perpendicular. This would result in a bond angle of 90°, in disagreement with observed values which are commonly close to the tetrahedral value of 109° 28'. The theory of bonding must explain both the number of bonds formed and the stereochemistry of the molecules. A satisfactory explanation requires the concept of the hybridization of atomic orbitals.

The simplest example of hybridization which can be considered is the formation of two covalent bonds by the element beryllium. In the ground state, the atom has the configuration $2s^2$, and the electrons are paired. Two unpaired electrons can be obtained only if one electron is promoted to a higher energy level, the most likely being that of nearest energy, i.e. a $2p$ orbital, conventionally chosen as $2p_x$. It can be shown easily that more extensive overlap with sigma type of symmetry can be obtained, and hence more stable bonding result, if these two atomic orbitals are replaced by two new orbitals 'compounded' from the simple orbitals. This is the process of hybridization. If the simple orbitals are represented as ψ_s and ψ_{p_x}, then the 'hybrid' orbitals are represented by:

$$\Psi_1 = \frac{1}{\sqrt{2}}(\psi_s + \psi_{p_x})$$

and
$$\Psi_2 = \frac{1}{\sqrt{2}}(\psi_s - \psi_{p_x})$$

A consequence of this process is that the electron probability, which is $\psi_s^2 + \psi_{p_x}^2$ before hybridization, is unchanged by the process, as can be shown by evaluating $\Psi_1^2 + \Psi_2^2$. The angular dependence of these hybrid orbitals can be found by simple vector addition as shown in Fig. 2.11. These hybrid orbitals tend to concentrate electrons on opposite sides of the nucleus, and require a bond angle of 180° instead of 90° if the maximum possible overlap is to result when two other atoms approach. Greater overlap, and hence stronger bonding, result from the stronger directional orientation of the hybrid orbitals. Although energy must be supplied to the system to promote an electron to the p_x orbital, this is more than compensated for by the energy given out when the two sigma bonds are formed.

The type of hybridization described above is known as sp hybridization from the atomic orbitals which are combined. This type is not found in bonding of the elements, but two other types which are, are important, i.e. sp^2 and sp^3. The former corresponds to three hybrid orbitals, the maximum extensions of which are directed towards the corners of an equilateral triangle, and affords a bond angle of 120°, whereas the latter

43

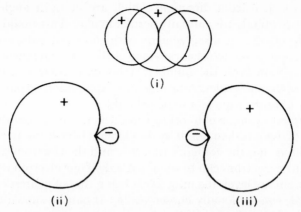

(i)

(ii)   (iii)

FIG. 2.11. The combination of s and p_x atomic orbitals to form two sp hybrid orbitals; (i) the constituent atomic orbitals, (ii) $s+p_x$, and (iii) $s-p_x$.

corresponds to four hybrid orbitals directed towards the corners of a regular tetrahedron, and affords a bond angle of 109° 28'.

The wave functions for these hybrid orbitals are given in Table 2.3, and the angular dependence of sp^2 orbitals is illustrated in Fig. 2.12. The functions as shown correspond to equivalent orbitals and hence to a regular geometry. However, if each orbital is not used identically in bonding, e.g. if one or more are occupied by non-bonding pairs of electrons (lone pairs), it might be expected that the bonding and non-bonding electron pairs would not be disposed regularly round the nucleus.

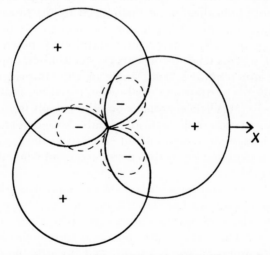

FIG. 2.12. The angular dependence of three sp^2 hybrid orbitals. These are derived in a manner analogous to that illustrated in the previous Figure for sp hybrid orbitals.

44

This is indeed so, and irregular geometry can be accounted for by slight modification of the coefficients in Table 2.3, so that, for example, one hybrid orbital may have somewhat more p character and less s character than another, provided that one or more of the other orbitals can accommodate this additional s character. Two hybrid orbitals with additional p character (of an sp^3 set) should afford a bond angle between 109° 28′ and 90°, which latter corresponds to pure p orbitals.

Table 2.3. Wave Functions for sp^2 and sp^3 Hybrid Orbitals

sp^2

$$\Psi_1 = \frac{1}{\sqrt{3}}\psi_s + \sqrt{\left(\frac{2}{3}\right)}\,\psi_{px}$$

$$\Psi_2 = \frac{1}{\sqrt{3}}\psi_s - \frac{1}{\sqrt{6}}\psi_{px} + \frac{1}{\sqrt{2}}\psi_{py}$$

$$\Psi_3 = \frac{1}{\sqrt{3}}\psi_s - \frac{1}{\sqrt{6}}\psi_{px} - \frac{1}{\sqrt{2}}\psi_{py}$$

sp^3

$$\Psi_1 = \tfrac{1}{2}(\psi_s + \psi_{px} + \psi_{py} + \psi_{pz})$$

$$\Psi_2 = \tfrac{1}{2}(\psi_s + \psi_{px} - \psi_{py} - \psi_{pz})$$

$$\Psi_3 = \tfrac{1}{2}(\psi_s - \psi_{px} - \psi_{py} + \psi_{pz})$$

$$\Psi_4 = \tfrac{1}{2}(\psi_s - \psi_{px} + \psi_{py} - \psi_{pz})$$

One molecule which can be described in this way will serve as an example. Sulphur has the electronic configuration s^2p^4 and is known to exist under various conditions as a cyclic S_8 molecule, in which each sulphur atom is bonded to two others. To use the localized molecular orbital approach, the electronic configuration of each sulphur atom can be written down as $(sp^3)_1^2(sp^3)_2^2(sp^3)_3^1(sp^3)_4^1$, i.e. four tetrahedrally distributed sp^3 hybrid atomic orbitals, two of which are singly occupied and of the correct symmetry to form bonds of sigma symmetry with two other sulphur atoms; the other two are doubly occupied and are non-bonding. The bond angle observed for this molecule in rhombic sulphur is 107° 55′, which is not appreciably different from the regular tetrahedral angle, and the difference can be interpreted as suggested in the previous paragraph.

There are some molecules in which the possibility of π overlap can be realized after the atomic arrangement has been explained by a sigma-bonded system. Ozone is such a molecule and will be considered later, but π overlap does not appear to be possible in the S_8 molecule. Bonding of this type could arise only if overlap were possible between an occupied orbital on one sulphur atom and a vacant d orbital on its neighbour. The occupied tetrahedral hybrid orbitals do not have the correct symmetry to allow this, and the possible overlap between an occupied $2p_z$ orbital on one atom and a vacant $3d_{zx}$ orbital on its neighbour seems unlikely since the $2p_z$ orbital is an inner orbital and is screened by outer occupied orbitals. (The discussion of this paragraph will be more easily understood after the following section has been read.)

(iii) **Polyatomic Molecules with Delocalized Orbitals.** An extreme case of a polyatomic molecule with delocalized orbitals is a single crystal of a metal where the 'molecule' comprises the total number of atoms in the crystal. In those molecules for which the localized orbital description can be used the arrangement of the atoms is dependent on the electronic configurations of the constituent atoms, as will be seen when the structures of the elements are considered below. In contrast, the atomic arrangements found in the metals often conform to one of three basic types (see later), and there is no obvious simple correspondence between the structure adopted and the atomic electronic configuration. Further, each atom has a high coordination number (number of nearest neighbours), and in many metals there are insufficient electrons to allow a pair to be situated between each pair of atoms. In view of these differences it is apparent that a different approach is required.

The simplest metal to consider is lithium which has the electronic configuration $1s^2 2s^1$. The inner electrons are of lower energy, are substantially localized, and are ignored in the following argument. If two lithium atoms approach sufficiently closely, their $2s$ orbitals overlap. Every lithium atom in a crystal of the solid has eight equidistant nearest neighbours (and a further six at a slightly greater distance), so that if overlap with one neighbouring orbital occurs then overlap with at least eight results. In a crystal of N atoms there are N $2s$ atomic orbitals and these are occupied by N valence electrons. Just as the overlap of two atomic orbitals results in the formation of two molecular orbitals separated by an energy gap (*cf.* hydrogen, Fig. 2.7), the overlap of N atomic orbitals results in N delocalized molecular orbitals all of which lie within this same energy gap. Each orbital is of different energy and since N in a crystal is very large, there is a very large number of different energy levels within this energy range; these energies must remain separate according to the quantum theory, but since there are so many discrete energy levels within the energy range they must be so close together as to represent almost a continuum of energy.

The precise distribution of the energies of these levels or orbitals within the energy band is also important. This distribution is usually represented graphically by a plot of $N(E)$ against E, where E is the magnitude of the energy, and $N(E)$ the number of energy states per very small unit increment of energy. If it is assumed that the potential field within the crystal in which the electrons move is homogeneous, a calculated distribution as shown in Fig. 2.13 (*a*) is obtained. At the absolute zero of temperature the N electrons in a crystal of lithium containing N molecular orbitals would occupy the $N/2$ orbitals of lowest energy, i.e. all the orbitals below E_{max}. At room temperature, however, a small proportion of the electrons would gain additional thermal energy, and would be promoted to higher levels since the levels within the band are sufficiently close, giving the distribution of Fig. 2.13 (*b*).

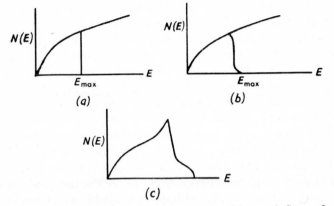

FIG. 2.13. Distribution of energy states, $N(E)$, within a band (see text). States of energy less than E_{max} are occupied by electrons.

More refined calculations, which do not assume a homogeneous field, lead to the distribution shown in Fig. 2.13 (*c*). Again only the lower half of these levels is occupied in a crystal of lithium. Bands with similar distributions of energy levels arise from the combination of atomic orbitals of higher energy, but these are unoccupied, just as are the appropriate atomic orbitals in an atom of lithium.

Before considering elements other than lithium, it is useful to consider how far the model described above can explain the characteristic properties of metals, and particularly electrical conductivity and optical behaviour. In the absence of an electrical field the electrons in the delocalized molecular orbitals will move in all directions so that the number moving in any given direction is equal to the number moving in the reverse of this direction. When, however, a potential difference is applied more electrons will flow in the direction of this applied field than in any other, and they acquire additional energy which allows them to be promoted to hitherto unoccupied orbitals. Thus an electrical current is conducted by the movement of electrons provided that there are energy levels of higher energy available to accommodate the electrons with this additional energy, at not too high an energy. It is clear from Fig. 2.13 (*c*) that this is so for lithium.

47

The moving electrons collide repeatedly with the positively charged ions and thereby lose energy, which appears as heat; as the temperature of the metal increases the thermal motion of the nuclei increases so that the chance of collision increases also, and accordingly the electrical conductivity decreases. This temperature dependence of electrical conductivity is an important criterion of metallic behaviour, and differentiates between metals and the class of materials known as semiconductors; the conductivity of semiconductors increases with increase of temperature, and this will be discussed further below.

The main optical characteristics of a metal are its opaqueness and the ability to reflect light. The electrons in the uppermost levels in a lithium crystal have vacant orbitals corresponding to a range of energies available to them so that incident radiation of all wavelengths can correspond to possible electronic transitions. This radiation is thus absorbed and does not penetrate the metal, which is accordingly opaque to visible light. A similar spectrum of radiation is emitted when the excited electrons fall back to the original levels, and hence the metal surface reflects the incident radiation. Thus the band of completely delocalized molecular orbitals of closely spaced energy explains conduction and optical behaviour, provided that vacant orbitals are available with energies close to these which are completely occupied, as in lithium.

When this argument is applied to a group II element such as beryllium with electronic configuration $2s^2$, it is seen that N atoms yield N orbitals and $2N$ electrons so that every level within the band is filled. A full band should result in the absence of electrical conductivity and of the absorption of all wavelengths of light unless the next higher band corresponding to the next higher atomic orbitals overlaps and extends the continuum of energy levels. It was seen above that the single energy of the $2s$ atomic orbital becomes a broad band ranging from lower than the original atomic orbital to higher; the atomic orbitals of higher energy show similar behaviour, and this can result in an overlap of bands. Two representations of this overlapping of energy bands are shown in Fig. 2.14. An insulator is a substance which has a full band separated from the next available energy band by an amount of energy too great to be overcome readily under the application of a potential difference.

Semiconductors are intermediate between metallic conductors and insulators; they possess an energy gap between two bands which is sufficiently small to be jumped by those electrons in the highest energy levels of the full band when these acquire thermal energy. In accordance with this, increase in temperature raises further electrons into the upper band, and since these electrons have available vacant orbitals in the upper band, they can carry an electrical current. The electrical conductivity thus increases with increase in temperature, in contrast to the

48

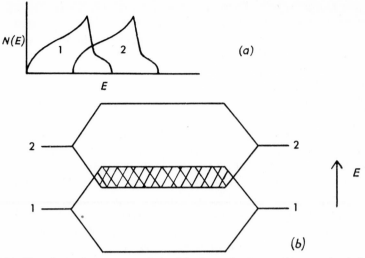

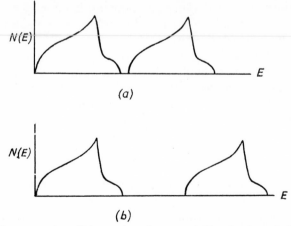

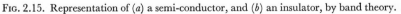

Fɪɢ. 2.14. Two alternative representations of the formation by atomic energy levels 1 and 2 of overlapping bands of energy.

behaviour of metallic conductors. Band diagrams to illustrate an insulator and a semi-conductor are shown in Fig. 2.15.

A study of X-ray emission spectra provides experimental evidence about the bands of energy levels described above. Whereas atomic spectra comprise sharp lines, each of a distinct wavelength and each representing a transition from one well defined energy state to another, X-ray spectra of metals show wide bands which cover a range of wavelengths and these correspond to transitions involving a band of closely

Fɪɢ. 2.15. Representation of (a) a semi-conductor, and (b) an insulator, by band theory.

49

adjacent energy levels. There are, however, in the X-ray spectra some sharp lines which indicate that the non-valence electrons which are of lower energy are in levels which are effectively those of the atomic orbitals. This assumption was made on p. 46. In X-ray crystallographic studies it is usual to use radiation of one accurately known wavelength, i.e. monochromatic radiation, and such radiation corresponds to a transition involving these inner electronic levels; an example is copper K_α radiation of wavelength 1·539 Å.

The band theory has been described above to explain metallic behaviour, but it has been seen that the behaviour of non-metals also can be described as that of materials in which an overlap of bands does not occur. This results in the absence of electrical conductivity and in different light absorption. The alternative approach to the bonding of the non-metallic elements which uses localized orbitals, and which was described in the previous section (pp. 42–46), is often more useful for the interpretation of chemical behaviour. It is important that either approach should be used, as appropriate. It was pointed out (p. 42) that it was an approximation to regard a molecular orbital as localized between two atoms; the band theory does not make this approximation.

The elements can be classified as (i) metallic conductors, (ii) semi-conductors, and (iii) non-metals or insulators. The elements of the Periodic Table in which s, d or f levels are being occupied by electrons, i.e. the s, d and f blocks, belong to the first class. The remaining p block comprises elements of all three classes, and indeed different allotropic modifications of several of these elements belong to different classes. It is well known that within the p block of the Periodic Table, metallic character increases with increase in atomic number, when the elements of a particular group are considered. Thus, for example, oxygen and sulphur are insulators, selenium is either an insulator or a semi-conductor according to its crystalline form, tellurium is a semi-conductor and polonium a metallic conductor.

The behaviour of the various forms will be considered when the elements are discussed individually, but it is appropriate at this point to give a general interpretation of this behaviour. The energies of transitions observed in certain series of atomic spectra can be represented by the expression:

$$E \propto R\left(\frac{1}{m^2} - \frac{1}{n^2}\right)$$

where R is a constant, and n and m are quantum numbers. It is clear that the difference in energy between adjacent electronic levels becomes smaller as the values for the adjacent quantum numbers become greater. Hence the difference in energy between the highest

50

occupied atomic orbital and the next higher vacant orbital decreases with increase in atomic number for elements within the same vertical group; the energy bands derived from these atomic orbitals when a crystal of the element is considered rather than free atoms, must also become closer together in the same sequence of elements; alternatively, the energy gap between these bands decreases and eventually disappears. In this way it is possible to explain the transition from a wide gap (insulator) in the lightest element, through a narrow gap (semi-conductor) to an overlap of bands (metallic conductor) in the heaviest element in a group.

(iv) **Some Molecules of an Intermediate Nature.** There are some forms of the elements which do not fit conveniently into one or other of the three sections described above, and some consideration will now be given to two of these, graphite and ozone. These will be discussed in more detail later, but the structures will be outlined here to illustrate the nature of the bonding.

In a crystal of graphite the atoms of carbon are arranged in a hexagonal pattern in planar sheets, so that each atom has three nearest neighbours and an inter-bond angle of 120° (Fig. 4.9). Each sheet is separated from the adjacent sheets by a distance which is appreciably greater than that between bonded atoms within a sheet. Graphite is black and has a low electrical conductivity which decreases with increase in temperature, i.e. metallic conduction.

The bond angle of 120°, as in the molecule of benzene, is accounted for by the assumption of sp^2 hybridization of the atomic orbitals of each carbon atom. Each carbon atom forms sigma bonds with its three neighbours using these hybrid orbitals, so that the localized orbital approach allows an interpretation of the stereochemistry of the structure. The remaining p orbital, conventionally regarded as the p_z orbital, is singly occupied and is able to overlap with the p_z orbitals of the three neighbouring atoms with pi symmetry. Since these overlap in turn with the corresponding orbitals of their neighbours, a completely delocalized pi system extends throughout the entire sheet. In this way all the valence electrons in the sheet are used in bonding and therefore no strong bonding can hold together the adjacent sheets. The completely delocalized pi system is directly analogous to delocalization as described above for the metallic elements, and can be regarded as forming a band of closely spaced molecular orbitals each of which can contain two electrons. It has been calculated that there is a slight overlap between this band and the vacant band of higher energy, so that conduction and optical properties similar to those of the metallic elements are thus explained. The conductivity is not high since at room temperature the concentration of the upper (conduction) band is only 10^{-4}–10^{-5} electrons per atom.

51

The molecule of ozone, O_3, is angular with a bond angle near to 120°, and this is again interpreted as the use of sp^2 hybrid orbitals by the central oxygen atom. When two of these overlap to form sigma bonds with appropriate orbitals on the remaining two oxygen atoms, the third is occupied by a non-bonding (or lone) pair of electrons. Now the remaining p_z orbital of the central oxygen atom is full, but those of the terminal oxygen atoms are singly occupied and all three are able to overlap so that, as in graphite delocalized pi bonding results, with electrons formally being donated by the central atom to the terminal atoms. The delocalized system comprises three atomic orbitals only, in contrast to an infinite number as in a graphite sheet or a metal crystal. Hence the band of energy levels comprises three orbitals only and since there are only four electrons, the lower two orbitals are occupied whereas the uppermost level is vacant.

SUMMARY

Chemical bonding in the elements can be understood with the help of the method of molecular orbitals, in which it is assumed that linear combinations of atomic orbitals are approximate solutions of the Schrödinger wave equation for systems containing more than one atom. The treatment of diatomic molecules, where a molecular orbital is described by two terms only, is modified for polyatomic systems by the assumption of localized orbitals, or completely delocalized orbitals as appropriate.

The bonding in individual elements will be considered later. Because of the structural differences between metals and non-metals as classes of elements, it is often convenient to consider them separately; it is perhaps appropriate to consider briefly at this point the factors which determine whether an element is a metal or a non-metal. The separations between atomic energy levels are such that the largest difference occurs when there is an increase in the principal quantum number, i.e. between the np level and the $(n+1)s$ level. Levels which have the same principal quantum number are closer together in energy. Also, as was indicated above, the separation between the np and $(n+1)$ s levels becomes smaller as n increases. The overlap of the bands formed from these atomic orbitals becomes more probable as the energy difference between successive atomic energy levels decreases. Accordingly the non-metallic elements, i.e. those which behave as insulators because there is no overlap between the highest full band and the next vacant band, are found only in the p block of the Periodic Table, since only in these elements does the next higher band have an increase in the principal quantum number.

Within the p block, metallic behaviour is observed in the heavier elements, as has been discussed above. It has been pointed out also that the formation of a molecular orbital requires the overlap of atomic orbitals. It is easy to visualize the overlap of the spherically symmetrical s atomic orbitals, and of the elongated p and d orbitals along the directions of their maximum extensions. It is more difficult to visualize the overlap of hybrid orbitals such as are used in the description of the structures of the non-metallic elements; when these overlap, the electrons are concentrated particularly between the two nuclei (with sigma symmetry) so that overlap in the opposite direction with a second atomic orbital, as is required if it is to contribute to the building up of a giant molecular orbital, is less likely.

As a consequence of this, as will be seen when the structures of the p block elements are described, the orbitals used in bonding become more nearly pure p orbitals as atomic number increases within a group of the Periodic Table; this strengthens the overlap which allows the formation of molecular orbitals and facilitates the metallic conduction which characterizes these elements.

CHAPTER 3

FUNDAMENTAL ASPECTS OF CRYSTAL STRUCTURE

It is the purpose of this Chapter to describe structural features of the elements in rather general terms, in order to facilitate detailed consideration of individual elements in the following Chapter. The division of the elements into metals on the one hand and non-metals on the other according to electrical conductivity was referred to in the preceding Chapter. It is convenient to use this classification again as a basis for a discussion of structural features.

THE STRUCTURE OF METALS

The electrical conductivity and optical properties of metals were interpreted by use of the electronic band theory, and some further

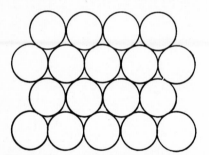

characteristic properties are readily explained by a consideration of structure, notably malleability, ductility and alloy formation (see below).

The atomic arrangements of many metals in the solid state conform to one or other of three patterns known as cubic close-packed, hexagonal close-packed and body-centred cubic respectively. In each of these, every atom

Fig. 3.1. The arrangement of spheres in a close-packed layer.

has a large number of nearest neighbours (coordination number) and the particular structure adopted by a given element does not appear to be determined in any simple manner by the electronic configuration of the atom.

The close-packing of spheres, as the term implies, is the most economical mode of packing possible. If a number of spheres is placed upon a plane surface and forces are applied so that they are under constraint, the arrangement adopted will be as close-packed as possible and will be as shown in Fig. 3.1, i.e. each sphere is surrounded by six others with which it is in contact, and these six are disposed towards the corners of a regular hexagon around a reference sphere. This pattern persists throughout an entire close-packed layer, and layers of this type are the basis of both the cubic and hexagonal close-packed structural patterns referred to above. The terms cubic and hexagonal refer to the symmetry of a three-dimensional lattice (see p. 4), and describe different overall symmetries found when such close-packed layers are stacked on top of each other in different sequences. (It should be noted that the hexagonal pattern of nearest neighbours described above for all close-packed layers is a feature of both cubic and hexagonal close-packing, and does not differentiate between them.)

When a second layer is stacked upon the first, it is clear that the greatest economy of space is achieved if each sphere of the second layer rests in a hollow made by three touching spheres of the first layer. These hollows are arranged in precisely the same pattern as the spheres, so that further spheres can be placed in the second layer in the same close-packed pattern as in the first layer. A portion of two such super-imposed layers is shown in Fig. 3.2.

Inspection of Fig. 3.2 shows that whereas the second layer rests on hollows on the first layer, there is also an entirely equivalent arrangement of hollows on the top of the first layer which is not occupied by the second layer. Since the second layer is close-packed, it is clear that no spheres can rest in this alternative set of hollows. The need to recognise it is seen when the orientation of the third layer with respect to the first two is considered. If the third layer is placed directly above the first layer, (and this corresponds with one of the alternative sets of hollows on the top of the second layer), the sequence can be described as *ABA*, and if maintained indefinitely this arrangement of spheres has hexagonal symmetry. This is the arrangement known as hexagonal close-packing.

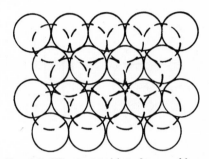

Fig. 3.2. The superposition of a second layer of close-packed spheres (dashed) upon a first such layer.

If, in contrast, the third layer is placed on top of the alternative set of hollows on the top of the second layer, then it is vertically above the hollows on the top of the first layer which were not occupied by the second layer; this is the sequence *ABC*. When the fourth layer lies above the first, and this sequence is continued indefinitely, it has cubic symmetry, and is the arrangement known as cubic close-packing.

It is a characteristic of a crystal which belongs to the hexagonal system, that the arrangement of atoms has a six-fold axis of symmetry; i.e. when rotated about this axis, the arrangement of atoms assumes an

55

identical orientation six times during a complete revolution. The six-fold axis of an arrangement of hexagonally close-packed atoms is at right angles to the planes of close-packing. Two representations of hexagonal close-packing are shown in Fig. 3.3.

It was stated in Chapter 1 that a hexagonal unit cell has $a = b \neq c$. The dimensions of a and c for a unit cell of atoms in hexagonal close-packing are indicated in Fig. 3.3; a and b are the distance between the centres of two touching spheres in one close-packed layer, whereas c is the perpendicular distance from the centre of one of these spheres to the centre of a sphere in the third layer directly below it. If the spheres are perfect, it can be shown that the ratio of c/a is 1·633. The unit cells of a number of metals which crystallize with this structure have a ratio close to this value, but some very large deviations are found also.

A cube does not possess a six-fold axis but has four three-fold axes

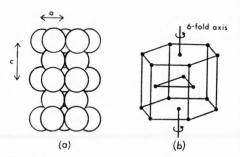

(a)   (b)

FIG. 3.3. Two representations of the hexagonal close-packing of spheres, showing (a) the dimensions a and c of the unit cell, and (b) the six-fold axis of symmetry normal to the close-packed planes.

which are the body diagonals of the cube, i.e. the lines from one corner to the diagonally opposite corner. When atoms are arranged in an *ABCA* sequence of close-packed layers it is seen that there is a three-fold axis perpendicular to the layers. It is difficult to visualize a cube when the layers are stacked in this way, since the layers are perpendicular to the body diagonal of the cube. The cube is not simple, but has an atom at the centre of each face, and hence the alternative description of this arrangement as face-centred cubic. Fig. 3.4 (a) shows a face-centred cube in its familiar orientation, and also (b) with its body-diagonal vertical to show layers of close-packed atoms. The close-packed layer can also be seen when a corner of the cube is removed, as in (d). It follows from the symmetry of the cube that such layers of close-packed atoms can be found in four different directions, i.e. normal to the four body-diagonals; this property illustrates the high symmetry of the cube, and no such feature occurs in the hexagonal system.

It can be seen from Fig. 3.1 that each atom has six nearest neighbours in one plane. In addition it is in contact with three atoms in the plane above and three in the plane below, so that whether the close-packing is cubic or hexagonal, each atom has twelve nearest neighbours. It might be expected that other close-packed sequences, perhaps less regular, than *ABABA* and *ABCABCA* would be found in the structures of metals, but

56

such are very uncommon. Two different sequences are found in the structures of certain lanthanide elements. The first of these is *ABACABACA*, etc., which produces overall hexagonal symmetry, and to differentiate from the sequence *ABABA* it is known as double hexagonal close-packing The second sequence is a more complex one, *ABABCBCACA*, in which the repeat unit is nine layers thick. The overall symmetry of this arrangement is rhombohedral.

The third common structural pattern adopted by metals is not related to close-packing, and is known as body-centred cubic. As the term indicates, there is an atom at the centre as well as at each corner of the cube. The coordination number of an atom in this structure is thus eight. When the structure is extended beyond one cube, it is seen that the next-to-nearest neighbours correspond to the centres of the adjacent cubes, and

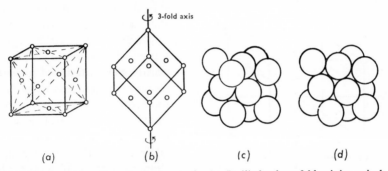

(a)   (b)   (c)   (d)

FIG. 3.4. Four representations of a face-centred cube. In (b) the three-fold axis is vertical and the close-packed layers horizontal. In (d) a corner has been removed to show an inclined close-packed layer.

hence are six in number. Since these are only 15% further removed, the coordination number is sometimes said to be fourteen. Fig. 3.5 shows an atom at the centre of a cube and indicates the positions of the six next-to-nearest neighbours.

The arrangement of atoms in layers in the structures of the metals makes it easy to understand why a lateral force should be able to cause deformation, i.e. by the sliding of one layer over another. Such deformation accounts for the characteristic malleability and ductility of metals, and it is significant that cubic metals are often more easily deformed than hexagonal metals since the former possess layering in a greater number of directions. The process of deformation is facilitated also by the mobility and delocalization of electrons in a metallic crystal, since these electrons can migrate and effect bonding with the atoms in their new positions. This is a less easy process in a crystal in which the electrons are appreciably localized, viz. in a non-metal.

57

5

Other properties often associated with metals are hardness, high melting and boiling points, and high density. Whereas the last is certainly due in part to the close-packing of metallic structures, it is influenced also by atomic radius and atomic weight. The other properties are indicative of particularly strong forces within the crystal, with no particular direction in which there is weaker bonding, as there is for example between molecules in a molecular lattice. Such strong bonding is not diagnostic of metals, as non-metals such as diamond are particularly hard and high-melting, whereas metals such as the alkalis, gallium and mercury are soft and low-melting.

One further property of the metallic elements is their ability to form alloys. The structural arrangements of the metallic elements, as described above, and the relative independence of structure from the electronic configuration of the atoms, make it easy to appreciate that the crystal lattice of one metal can incorporate some atoms of a second metal provided that there is not too large a difference in atomic size; such a difference would impose a strain on the crystal lattice. If the incorporated element has a different electronic configuration from that of the host, a change in the electrical conductance is to be expected since the conduction band will become more or less full according as the incorporated atoms have more or fewer electrons.

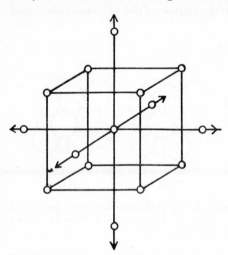

FIG. 3.5. A body-centred cube, showing the six next-to-nearest neighbours.

A number of allotropic transformations shown by the metallic elements involve a change from one of the three 'key' structures to another. There are three such possible transformations:

(i) Cubic close-packed (face-centred cubic) $\rightleftharpoons$ hexagonal close-packed

(ii) Body-centred cubic $\rightleftharpoons$ hexagonal close-packed

(iii) Body-centred cubic $\rightleftharpoons$ face-centred cubic

The structural interrelationship of the two close-packed forms is readily visualized, since it involves only a difference in the sequence of stacking of close-packed layers, whereas the interrelationship between the pairs of structures of (ii) and (iii) above is less obvious.

58

The precise mechanism by which one form of a metal transforms into another is seldom if ever known, but suggested mechanisms for (ii) and (iii) are considered below, partly to illustrate the structural inter-relationship, and for (ii) to illustrate the mechanism by which a martensitic transformation may proceed.

STRUCTURAL INTER-RELATIONSHIPS

Body-centred Cubic and Hexagonal Close-packed Lattices. In Fig. 3.6 are shown a body-centred cubic unit cell and the unit cell of a

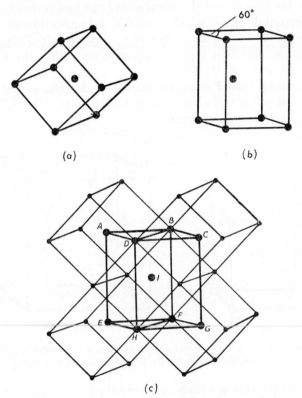

FIG. 3.6. (*a*) A body-centred unit cell; (*b*) a unit cell of hexagonal close-packed lattice; (*c*) five body-centred unit cells, linked to show relationship to a monoclinic cell which is transformed by shear to a hexagonal cell (see text).

hexagonal close-packed lattice. Note that the atom in the body of the hexagonal cell is not at the body-centre. (Reference to Fig. 3.3 (*a*) shows that it is situated directly above the centre of a triangle comprising three of the four atoms in the base of the cell.) In Fig. 3.6 (*c*) are shown five body-centred cubes (in the same orientation); a new cell is picked out,

59

bounded by atoms *A, B, C, D, E, F, G* and *H*, with *I* at the centre; *A, C, E, G* and *I* were centres of the original body-centred cubes. It can be calculated, that if the length of the original cubic unit cells is x, the axis *AE* of the new cell has a length of $\sqrt{(2)}x$, and the axes *AB* and *AD* have length $\sqrt{(3)}/2x$. This cell has monoclinic symmetry, since the angle $\angle BAD$ has a value of 70° 32'; the axial ratio is 1·63, as required for a hexagonal unit cell. Two changes are necessary, for the monoclinic cell to become hexagonal; the angle $\angle BAD$ requires to be 60°, and atom *I* must be translated from the body-centre. The angle can be modified by a shear of the plane *DCGH* through a slight distance in the direction of *DC*, and modification of the position of *I* can be effected by the shear of the horizontal plane which contains it, again through a small distance only. Thus two shear movements can produce the necessary transformation, which is typically martensitic within the description given in Chapter 1 (pp. 24–26).

Body-centred and Face-centred Cubic Lattices. The transformation described for this change (referred to on p. 23) is dilatational, and is not martensitic in character.

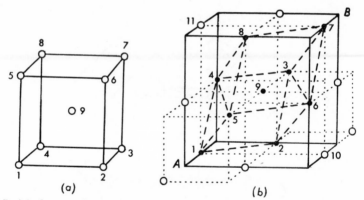

Fig. 3.7. A body-centred cube before and after a distortion which produces a transformation of first coordination, yielding a face-centred cubic structure.

In Fig. 3.7 (*a*) is shown a body-centred cube with its atoms numbered; atoms 1–8 represent the corners, and atom 9 is at the centre. The 110 plane contains atoms 2, 4, 6, 8 and 9, so that each atom in this plane has four neighbours within the plane. When the cube is suitably elongated along the body-diagonal which passes through atoms 1, 9 and 7 (a three-fold axis of the cube), the atoms take up new positions and it is found that the nine atoms are then arranged in sites which correspond to a face-centred cubic lattice. The elongation of the cube is the dilatation. The face-centred cubic lattice is shown in Fig. 3.7 (*b*). The nine atoms under

60

consideration are shown as solid circles, whereas the additional atoms required to complete the new cube are shown as open circles. This face-centred cube is shown in bold lines and is drawn so that the edge-centre of Fig. 3.4 (*a*) has become a corner, i.e. the origin of the cube is transposed by half the length of the unit cell in all three directions.

Atoms 3 and 5 are situated on extensions of the cube, and these extensions are indicated by dotted lines. The original body-centred cube is indicated by dashed lines. Inspection shows that atom 9 is at the centre of the new cube as of the original; atoms 2, 4, 6, 8 and 9 are in a 111 plane of the new cube. Atoms 10 and 11 which originally were at the centres of cubes adjacent to the one under consideration, and hence 15% further from atom 9 than atoms 2, 4, 6 and 8, are equidistant from it in the face-centred cube, so that atom 9 has the six nearest neighbours required in a close-packed layer. This layer is normal to the body-diagonal *AB*. It has already been pointed out that this transformation results in a change in the primary coordination of an atom, from eight to twelve.

There are, of course, a number of metallic transformations which are not between two of the three forms described above, e.g. the transformations of plutonium or mercury, etc. Examples of the types of change described in detail in the previous pages are, however, relatively numerous as will be seen in Chapter 4.

NON-METALS

The non-metallic elements are in Groups IV-VIII of the Periodic Table, with the exception of several of the heavier members of these groups, and with the inclusion of boron from Group III, and hydrogen. It is characteristic of these elements that they have a low coordination number in their crystal structure, in contrast to the structures of the metallic elements. This coordination number is usually $(8-N)$, where N is the number of the group of the Periodic Table in which the element is found. The number 8 is the number of electrons required to fill completely the s and p orbitals; $(8-N)$ is the number of vacancies in the p orbitals of an atom of the element and hence represents the maximum number of electron pair sigma bonds which the atom can form with like atoms, without the use of orbitals of higher energy.

Because of the implications of the $(8-N)$ rule, it is appropriate to discuss the bonding in non-metallic elements using the localized molecular orbital approach, as discussed on p. 42. When an atom forms $(8-N)$ sigma bonds, it follows that all its s and p orbitals are completely occupied, and accordingly the stereochemistry of the element (in the elementary state) results from the use of sp^3 hybrid (or less often pure p),

61

atomic orbitals, and the sigma overlap of these with comparable orbitals of the appropriate number of neighbouring atoms.

An atom of a Group VIII element has no vacancies in p orbitals and in accordance with the $(8-N)$ rule forms no electron pair bonds with other atoms of its own kind. Only weak cohesive forces can hold the atoms together, so the elements are monatomic, and gaseous, under normal conditions. When they solidify at low temperatures, the effectively spherical atoms assume the arrangement of close-packing, but without the interatomic distance becoming very small. An atom of a Group VII element has one vacancy in the p orbitals, and can form one electron pair bond with the formation of a diatomic molecule. Again the molecules are held together by weak forces only, and the halogens are volatile elements.

Atoms of Groups V and VI elements have three and two vacancies respectively in the p orbitals, and can thus form three or two sigma bonds with other atoms. This allows the formation of monomeric species, e.g. the P_4 and the S_8 molecules, but also allows the formation of an infinitely large molecule, or high polymer. The allotropy of the elements of these groups arises because of these possible structural alternatives. The inter-bond angles observed in the structures of these elements vary from the regular tetrahedral angle of $109° \ 28'$ when the hybrid orbitals are exactly equivalent, to $90°$ when pure p orbitals are used. Intermediate angles correspond to a greater or lesser contribution to the hybridization by the s orbital. Just as there is an attractive force due to electron pairing which contributes to the decrease in the energy of the system, to the stability of the resultant molecule and to the close approach of the atoms, so also there is a repulsive force due to the close approach of the electron pairs in the non-bonding hybrid orbitals of adjacent atoms; as was seen in Fig. 2.1, the equilibrium distribution of the atoms, i.e. the shape and interatomic distances of the molecule, depends upon the balance between these attractive and repulsive, and any other, forces.

Atoms of the Group IV elements have four vacancies in the p orbitals, and can form four sigma bonds, an arrangement which yields only polymeric structures in the elements. There are no non-bonding pairs of valence electrons. The physical properties of giant molecules, or polymers, are very different from those of small molecules. Polymeric molecules, on account of their large mass, require appreciable thermal energy to acquire the mobility which characterizes the liquid state, and this is applicable even more strongly to the gaseous state. In consequence the polymeric molecules have high melting and boiling points, and are very involatile. Most of the polymeric forms of the elements undergo melting or boiling with breakdown into smaller molecules, and such processes occur at the temperature at which these smaller molecules become the thermodynamically stable form of the element. Another

62

physical property which differentiates between monomer and polymer is solubility. The insolubility of the large molecules must be explained in a manner similar to their high melting points; it is difficult to visualize 'holes' in a liquid which would allow it to act as solvent for molecules of considerable size. The low electrical conductivity of elements in Groups IV–VII has been referred to in terms of band theory during the discussion of metals, and in particular the transition within a group of elements from insulator through semi-conductor to true metal. Electronic conductivity throughout an entire crystal is possible only when the molecule is quasi-infinite, since the intermolecular distances between discrete molecules are too large to allow electron jumps. It is well known that as the transition from insulator to true metal occurs, the ratio of intermolecular atomic distance/intramolecular atomic distances decreases.

Exceptions to the $(8 - N)$ rule are graphite (see p. 51) and the diatomic molecules of oxygen and nitrogen (see pp. 41–42). In each of these, it has been seen that pi bonding contributes to the stability of the molecule, and that each atom of the element forms $(8 - N)$ bonds, but since the number of bonds to each neighbouring atom is greater than one, the number of neighbouring atoms must be less than $(8 - N)$. The existence of other molecules in which pi bonding makes a contribution might also be expected, but bonds of this symmetry derived from parent p atomic orbitals (denoted $p\pi$—$p\pi$) are uncommon except between atoms of elements of the first row of the Periodic Table. Presumably the p orbitals in atoms of other elements are too far apart to overlap appreciably and without such overlap the bond is less favourable energetically. The diatomic S_2 molecule is an example of a heavier element with such pi bonding, but it is thermodynamically very unstable except at very high temperatures. Pi bonding can also arise by the overlap of d orbitals $(d\pi$—$d\pi)$, but the d orbitals of the main group elements are always full, so that no such additional overlap occurs in these elements.

To summarize, the majority of structures of the non-metallic elements comprise molecules in which each atom is bonded by $(8 - N)$ sigma bonds to $(8 - N)$ neighbouring atoms using sp^3 hybrid atomic orbitals. Some of these molecules are monomeric, others polymeric. In relatively few molecules pi bonding also occurs, when the number of bonds formed per atom remains $(8 - N)$, but the number of neighbouring atoms falls correspondingly. In the heavier elements, as metallic character increases, the orbitals used in bonding tend from sp^3 hybrid to pure p orbitals.

THE STRUCTURES OF ZINC BLENDE AND SODIUM CHLORIDE

Although the structures of zinc blende—the cubic form of zinc sulphide—and sodium chloride are those of binary compounds, it is

necessary to refer to various aspects of these in the descriptions of structures of the elements. Accordingly it is convenient to discuss them in
some detail in this section on more general structural aspects. The
structures are related to the face-centred cubic arrangement which was
shown in Fig. 3.4.

Both the structure of zinc blende and that of sodium chloride can be
described as two equivalent inter-penetrating face-centred cubic lattices,
but they differ one from another in the mode of interpenetration. In the
structure of zinc blende each atom is surrounded tetrahedrally by four
atoms which belong to the alternative lattice, whereas in the structure of
sodium chloride each atom is surrounded octahedrally by six such atoms.
In a simple face-centred cubic lattice each atom can be considered to be
in contact with its twelve equidistant nearest neighbours, and the lattice
is close-packed; when two such lattices interpenetrate, however, each

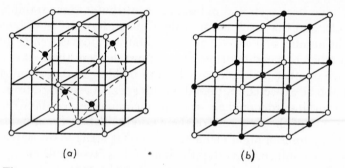

(*a*)   (*b*)

Fig. 3.8. The structures of (*a*) zinc blende, and (*b*) sodium chloride, related to a face-centred
cube.

atom is in contact with four or six atoms in the alternative inter-penetrating lattice, so that the twelve neighbours in its own lattice are somewhat
further distant and no longer in contact with it. Each face-centred cubic
lattice in such a situation has the same pattern of arrangement as that of
cubic close-packing, but cannot be described as truly close-packed.

It is useful to consider the structures of zinc blende and sodium
chloride in two alternative ways, corresponding directly to the two
representations of the face-centred cube shown in Fig. 3.4 (*a*) and (*b*). In
Fig. 3.8 the two structures are shown such that the orientation of Fig.
3.4 (*a*) can be seen. In each case the atoms of the different lattices are
shown by open and closed circles respectively, and in each compound
the one lattice is occupied by metal atoms and the other by non-metal
atoms. The four neighbours which surround one atom in the zinc blende
lattice occupy one corner and three face-centres of the cube of the
alternative lattice. In the sodium chloride structure the atom at the

64

body-centre of the cube is surrounded by six neighbours of the alternative lattice each of which is sited at a face-centre, whereas an atom at the mid-point of a cube edge has four such neighbours sited at face-centres and two at corners of the cube.

When the two lattices of the zinc blende structure are occupied by atoms of the same element, the structure is known as the diamond structure and is adopted not only by that form of carbon, but also by silicon, germanium and one form of tin. When the two lattices of the sodium chloride structure are occupied by atoms of the same element, the structure of β-polonium is obtained.

An alternative approach to these structures reveals layers of atoms in the familiar close-packed type of array (though no longer truly close-packed, as pointed out above), arranged horizontally. This corresponds with the orientation of the face-centred cube as shown in Fig. 3.4 (*b*).

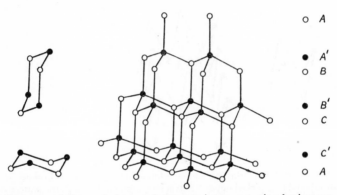

○	*A*
●	*A'*
○	*B*
●	*B'*
○	*C*
●	*C'*
○	*A*

FIG. 3.9. Structure of diamond. Atoms of alternate interpenetrating lattices are shown as ○ and ●, but are all of carbon. The six-membered rings are shown separately in the same orientations.

Whereas the sequence of layers in a simple face-centred cubic lattice is *ABCABCA* (p. 56), the structures under consideration comprise two interpenetrating lattices and have alternate layers from alternate lattices. The diamond structure can then be described as having the sequence of layers *AA' BB' CC' A*, etc. (Fig. 3.9), where *A*, *B* and *C* denote different possible orientations of the layers with respect to one another (as in *ABCABCA*), and the 'dash' indicates a layer originating from the alternative lattice. Thus the second layer is immediately below the first, the fourth below the third, etc. On this notation the β-polonium structure is denoted as *AC' BA' CB' A*, so that the fourth layer is immediately below the first, but originates from the alternative lattice.

In Fig. 3.9 is shown the diamond structure with the close-packed type of layers horizontal. Three features should be noted; (i) the invariable

65

tetrahedral coordination, (ii) the exact superposition of alternate layers from alternate lattices, and (iii) the arrangement throughout the entire structure of six-membered rings in the chair configuration. These six-membered rings arise from the superposition of two layers, and hence are also seen in structures based on the sodium chloride structure. The correspondence of the representation of Fig. 3.9 with the unit cube is difficult to see; it should be recalled, however, that Fig. 3.9 is related to Fig. 3.8 (*a*) as Fig. 3.4 (*b*) to Fig. 3.4 (*a*).

INTER-RELATIONSHIP OF THE POLYMERIC STRUCTURES
OF THE ELEMENTS OF GROUPS IV, V AND VI

The $(8-N)$ rule requires four-coordination for a Group IV element, and the diamond lattice allows such Group IV elements to have an

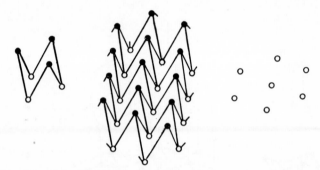

FIG. 3.10. A corrugated double layer of atoms as found in the structure of bismuth, etc. On the left, a six-membered ring picked out of the structure, and, on the right, the pattern of a close-packed type of layer.

infinite polymeric structure. Similarly, coordinations of three and two are required for Groups V and VI elements respectively. The heaviest element of Group VI, polonium, has the somewhat unexpected coordination number of six, and as seen above, can readily be described as related in structure to sodium chloride. The polymeric structures of the Group V and the remaining Group VI elements can also be described as related to the sodium chloride structure. The connection is less obvious and is described below. Thus all the polymeric structures of the Groups IV, V and VI elements can be traced to a common link in the face-centred cube.

When two close-packed type of layers are superimposed, each atom has three nearest neighbours in the other layer. Such an arrangement can be described as a corrugated double layer, and this is illustrated in Fig. 3.10. The atoms of the two separate close-packed type of layers are shown differently. The hexagonal pattern of such a layer can be seen, as can the six-membered, chair-configuration rings. The nature of this double layer can be varied by change in the inter-bond angle, and the complete three-dimensional structure can be varied by change in the ratio,

distance from one atom to its nearest neighbour in the next double layer
───
distance from that atom to its nearest neighbour within the double layer

If the interbond angle is 90° and the ratio is 1·0, the β-polonium structure is obtained, and three nearest neighbours become six, since the three in

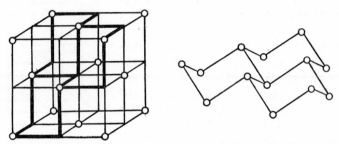

Fig. 3.11. The relationship of the layer structure shown in the previous Figure to that of the sodium chloride structure. The right-hand diagram can be compared with Fig. 3.10 and is a portion of the left-hand diagram in a different orientation.

the adjacent double layer are as near as the three in the same layer. As soon as the angle becomes greater than 90° and the ratio greater than 1·0, the number of nearest neighbours is three only, and the structures of the Group V elements bismuth, antimony and arsenic are described in this way.

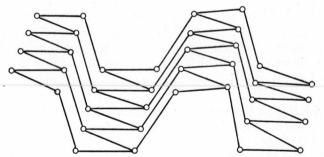

Fig. 3.12. Puckered double layer as found in the structure of black phosphorus.

The chair-form rings are joined to their neighbours in the *cis* conformation in this structure. A sodium chloride unit cube is illustrated in Fig. 3.11 with the points joined to show this form of layer structure running through the cube.

The six-membered rings can, of course, link in the *trans* conformation, and there is an alternative structure found in black phosphorus, where the linkage is sometimes *cis* and sometimes *trans*. This leads to a double layer which looks very different from that of Fig. 3.10, and is shown in Fig. 3.12, whereas the relationship to the sodium chloride cube is shown in Fig. 3.13, which should therefore be compared with Fig. 3.11, where the corresponding all-*cis* conformation is shown. Once again this structure is not identical with that of sodium chloride, since in phosphorus the bond angle is not 90° and the distance ratio is greater than 1·0. This difference between the structures of black phosphorus on the one hand, and certain forms of the heavier congeners of Group V on the other, is a particularly subtle one.

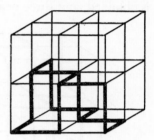

To appreciate the relationship of the structures of the Group VI elements to the structure of sodium chloride, it is necessary to consider the representation of parallel layers of close-packed type. In Fig. 3.14 (*a*) are shown four such layers in the arrangement corresponding to the sequence *AC′ BA′*. The atoms numbered 1–8 define a regular cube which is exactly one-eighth of that shown in Fig. 3.8, and this smaller cube becomes the unit of structure when the atoms

Fig. 3.13. A portion of the structure of Fig. 3.12 drawn with bond angles of 90° to illustrate the relation to a regular cube. Note the conformation of the six-membered rings.

of both interpenetrating lattices are identical; this is the situation when the structures of elements are considered.

In Fig. 3.14 (*b*) is shown a projection of these four layers in a direction at right angles to the plane of the layers; the atoms are numbered identically to facilitate identification. Since the structural arrangement as shown in Figs. 3.14 (*a*) and (*b*) is regular cubic, each atom has six equidistant nearest neighbours, three in the plane below and three in the plane above that in which it is situated. To obtain a structural pattern related to this, but such that each atom has only two nearest neighbours, one below and one above, each layer must be translated slightly with respect to the others; this translation must be such that of the three atoms in an adjoining layer to the reference atom, one becomes nearer and the other two farther removed.

The directions in which these distortions must proceed are indicated in Fig. 3.14 (*b*). The projection of the resultant atomic arrangement is shown in Fig. 3.14 (*c*). Whereas atom 1 was equidistant from atoms 2, 3 and 4 in Fig. 3.14 (*a*) and (*b*), in Fig. 3.14 (*c*) it is closer to atom 2 but further from atoms 3 and 4. When the atomic arrangement is seen in the orientation of Fig. 3.14 (*d*) the atoms are seen to be arranged in chains, i.e. each atom has two nearest neighbours, whereas the remaining four are slightly further distant. Such chain structures are found for forms of sulphur, selenium and tellurium. It can be seen in Fig. 3.14

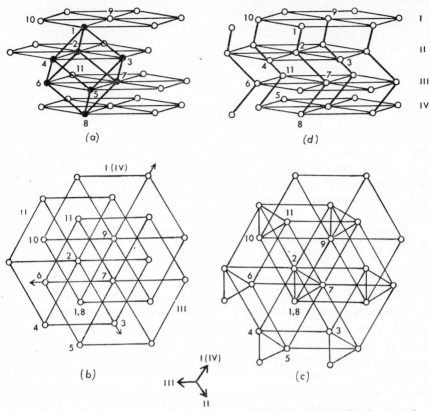

FIG. 3.14. Four layers of a sodium chloride structure (*a*), and in projection (*b*); the same after translations as indicated, in (*d*) and (*c*) to illustrate chain formation.

(*c*) that these chains are arranged in the pattern of close-packing, and Fig. 3.15 illustrates this point more clearly.

The extent of the distortion of the cubic lattice to give individual

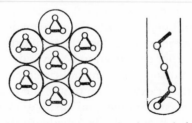

FIG. 3.15. To illustrate the close-packed arrangement of chains, arranged as in Fig. 3.14 (*c*) and (*d*)

chains modifies the inter-bond angle and the 'distance ratio' in a manner similar to that discussed in relation to the structures of the Group V elements. The greater the distortion from the regular cubic arrangement, the larger becomes the ratio and the larger the inter-bond angle.

CHAPTER 4

THE ALLOTROPIC ELEMENTS

In the remaining portion of the book those elements which can be obtained in more than one allotropic form will be considered in turn. They are treated in the sequence of the Periodic Table according to their electronic configurations, in four sections:

(i) the s block;
(ii) the d block (excluding Sc, Y and La);
(iii) the f block (including Sc, Y and La);
(iv) the p block.

A feature of the ensuing discussion which must be emphasized strongly is the lack of unanimity in the chemical literature as to the authenticity of numerous allotropes and of the precise values of physical data. It is not appropriate in a book of this scope to discuss every point of view, and it follows that personal, critical selection of material has been necessary on occasions, so that some readers will find points with which they disagree.

It is not altogether surprising that such a situation should have arisen. The criteria used for the characterization of a completely distinct phase have not always been as reliable as at the present day, and the non-crystalline nature of some forms creates difficulty even for the characterization by modern X-ray crystallographic methods. Further, it is likely that many experimental data have been compiled using materials of inadequate purity. There is abundant evidence in recent work that changes in behaviour can be brought about by impurities; modern techniques have facilitated not only the preparation of purer materials than was possible previously, but also the verification of that purity. In consequence some earlier data need to be revised.

The study of the allotropy of the metallic elements is perhaps affected by impurities to a greater extent than that of the non-metallic elements. The techniques of crystallization and distillation which can be particularly useful for the more volatile, covalently bonded, elements are less readily applied to metals, so that these are often more difficult to obtain in a state of high purity. The removal of the last traces of oxygen, nitrogen, carbon, etc., from highly reactive metals is not always a simple matter; it is indeed the structural nature of metallic lattices, which allows the incorporation of such small atoms, and alloy formation,

70

which makes purification more difficult. It is worthy of note, also, that a quoted analytical purity can be misleading since a relatively low percentage of impurity by weight can conceal an appreciable percentage of impurity atoms, if these atoms are of low atomic weight compared with the host atoms.

In the accounts of allotropy which follow, the greatest emphasis is placed upon a description of the structures of the various forms and their relative stabilities. Space does not allow a complete coverage of the subject matter, and many physical data, such as entropies, free energies, latent heats of transformation, etc., have been omitted unless they serve to illustrate a feature of particular importance. Perhaps less detail is devoted to the metallic elements than to the non-metals, since the state of theoretical knowledge is less able to explain why a particular metal has a particular structure. It is a feature of the metallic elements that many of their modifications cannot be isolated under normal conditions; this, to some extent, detracts from their interest to chemists, and makes their study more difficult.

THE *S* BLOCK ELEMENTS

The stable crystal form of all the alkali metals under normal conditions is the body-centred cubic structure, although of the group II elements only the heaviest, barium, adopts this structure: i.e. this form is more commonly found when the *s* level is half filled than when completely full; it is found also, in particular, in transition elements which have a *d* level less than half full. The other group II elements and the later transition elements more commonly adopt close-packed lattices. On thermodynamic grounds (p. 23) the body-centred cubic structure is likely to be a high temperature form, on account of its openness compared with the close-packed lattices, and indeed examples discussed below indicate that this is so.

The only characterized allotropic forms of the alkali metals (i.e. omitting any obtained by the action of high pressures) were found by Barrett, when he argued from such a premise as the above that alternative forms of the alkalis would be found only at low temperatures. Both lithium and sodium have now been obtained in hexagonal and cubic close-packed forms, but efforts to obtain such forms for the remaining alkali metals have been unsuccessful.

When **lithium** is cooled to the temperature of liquid nitrogen (77° K), a spontaneous transformation occurs and a hexagonally close-packed form is obtained. The process shows all the characteristics of a martensitic transformation, i.e. the complete change requires a range of temperature, so that the amount of the hexagonal form obtained increases as the temperature is lowered, although the change is incomplete even at 5° K, and the reverse process occurs only over a slightly higher temperature range. Under suitable conditions the transformation is accompanied by audible clicks as a number of atoms of one plane move simultaneously. Although the form is described as hexagonal, the stacking sequence is found to have numerous faults and irregularities. The same process, with the same characteristics and symmetry of the product, was later found for **sodium** although it was detected only at temperatures below 36° K. In view of this difference in temperature of the onset of these two transformations, it is not surprising that no similar transformations were observed for the other elements.

The cubic close-packed forms of lithium and sodium were obtained at similar temperatures to those at which the spontaneous changes described above were found to start. They were obtained, however, by cold-working the metals at these temperatures. It is believed that a martensitic transformation begins only at a temperature slightly below that at which the high temperature form becomes thermodynamically unstable. The application of mechanical energy at a temperature at which the body-centred form is metastable allows the energy barrier of the transition to be overcome. The transition in the reverse direction can be effected, presumably, by cold-working at a slightly higher temperature, or by the input of sufficient thermal energy. The close-packed form of lithium reverts to the body-centred form above 150° K, and the corresponding change in sodium at a somewhat lower temperature.

Of the group II elements, beryllium, calcium and strontium are believed to be obtainable in more than one crystalline form. Under normal conditions **beryllium** exists in a hexagonally close-packed form. There is a particularly confused literature concerning possible transformations at elevated temperatures; there is, however, an appreciable measure of agreement that a transformation takes place at about 1260°, i.e. 40° below the melting point of the metal; the structure of such a high temperature form might well be body-centred cubic.

It has been reported that both **calcium** and **strontium** are trimorphic, with a close parallel in behaviour between the two. The corresponding data are as follows:

Cubic close-packed		Hexagonal close-packed		Body-centred cubic
Calcium	250°		464°	
Strontium	235°		540°	

Smith and Bernstein, however, in a recent paper have put forward evidence that the hexagonal close-packed form of calcium can be obtained only if the metal is impure, and contains particularly some hydrogen. If this evidence is accepted, calcium must be regarded as

72

dimorphic only, with the rejection of the hexagonal form as an allotrope of calcium. It would then be appropriate to consider the validity of the corresponding form of strontium. The transition from a cubic to a hexagonal close-packed form is not common among the metals.

THE d BLOCK ELEMENTS

Those transition elements which can be obtained in more than one form are situated particularly at the left-hand side of the Periodic Table and in the first long period, i.e. elements which have relatively few electrons in their d level, or which have small atoms. When scandium, yttrium and lanthanum are excluded, to be considered along with the chemically similar lanthanides, there remain ten elements to be discussed in this section, titanium, zirconium, hafnium, thorium, chromium, tungsten, manganese, iron, cobalt and mercury, and some doubt has been cast upon the alternative forms of two of these, chromium and tungsten. Of the remaining eight, six transform to a body-centred cubic structure as the high temperature form, the exceptions being cobalt and mercury.

Titanium, zirconium and **hafnium** have hexagonal close-packed lattices at normal temperatures, whereas **thorium**, the heaviest element of the group, is cubic, but all four transform to the body-centred cubic structure, the temperatures commonly quoted being titanium 883° C, zirconium 862°, hafnium 1760° and thorium 1400°. The transformations of the first three are believed to be martensitic.

No alternative forms are known for the vanadium group of elements which, except for protactinium, have body-centred cubic lattices. By analogy with the alkali metals, it would seem that any alternative allotropic forms would be stable only at low temperatures. Chromium, molybdenum and tungsten also adopt the body-centred cubic structure, but alternative forms of chromium and tungsten require consideration also. No fewer than three alternative forms of **chromium** have been prepared—hexagonal and cubic close-packed and one form iso-structural with alpha-manganese—but always by electrolytic preparative methods where conditions must be carefully controlled. Each of these forms transforms at room temperature to the normal body-centred cubic form, and must therefore be metastable. It has been suggested that they are not pure chromium, and even that they are hydrides of the element. It seems doubtful that they should be considered as true allotropes.

Very similar remarks apply to the second form of **tungsten** known as beta-tungsten. This also must be prepared under controlled conditions, in particular at temperatures below 600° above which it transforms. It has been claimed that this material cannot be obtained unless the lattice

73

contains at least a small proportion of oxygen atoms. The structure of beta-tungsten has been known for many years, and other materials are known to be isostructural with it. It is based on a body-centred cube, but with two additional atoms on each face. There are two types of non-equivalent site in such a lattice (Fig. 4.1).

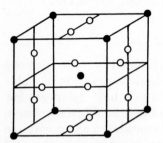

Manganese has a complex crystallography despite its simple electronic configuration of a half-filled d level, and in contrast to technetium and rhenium, which exist only in hexagonal close-packed forms. There are four known forms, of which the alpha and beta have complicated structures (not illustrated) both with cubic symmetry.

FIG. 4.1. Structure of β-tungsten.

Whereas body-centred and face-centred cubic lattices have two and four atoms in the unit cell respectively, alpha- and beta-manganese have fifty-eight and twenty respectively. These lattices, like that of beta-tungsten, also have various non-equivalent lattice sites. The various transitions are as shown:

$$\underset{\text{(cubic)}}{\alpha} \xrightarrow[]{700°} \underset{\text{(cubic)}}{\beta} \xrightarrow[]{1080°} \underset{\substack{\text{(cubic close-}\\\text{packed)}}}{\gamma} \xrightarrow[]{1140°} \underset{\substack{\text{(body-centred}\\\text{cubic)}}}{\delta}$$

The alpha–beta transition is said to be extremely sluggish, and indeed it is difficult to visualize a mechanism by which the one form could change to the other. In consequence the beta form can be obtained in metastable condition at room temperature. The two higher-temperature transformations take place readily, and hence these forms cannot be cooled unchanged to room temperature. It has been shown that the gamma form can be obtained at ordinary conditions by an electrolytic preparation, but transforms into the stable alpha form. At one time it was believed that the gamma form had a face-centred tetragonal unit cell at lower temperatures and that the c dimension changed with increase in temperature so that the structure became face-centred cubic (cubic close-packed) at higher temperatures, but it seems to be established now that it is face-centred cubic throughout the entire temperature range.

The presence of impurity atoms can often have a profound effect upon the temperature and rate of a transformation. One result of this is that a transition can be retarded to such an extent that a high-temperature form can be obtained at ordinary temperatures, even although it normally transforms so rapidly that it cannot be chilled to room temperature without reverting to the low temperature form. The gamma and delta forms of manganese can be stabilized in this way.

74

The allotropy of **iron** is well known and shows unusual features. Under no conditions has it been obtained in the stable form of its congeners ruthenium and osmium, i.e. hexagonal close-packed, and the low-temperature form is body-centred cubic. The alpha (body-centred cubic) form transforms to the gamma, cubic close-packed, form at about 910°C, and this in turn changes back to a body-centred cubic form, the delta form, at about 1390°. There is a well-known second-order transformation in the temperature range 750°–790°, when the element changes from a ferromagnetic to a paramagnetic state, due to a change in alignment of nuclear spins rather than to a change in atomic positions in the crystal lattice. In the temperature range between this transition and the transformation to the gamma form, the element is referred to as beta-iron, but has the same crystal structure as alpha-iron.

Apart from iron, only cerium can exist in the same crystal form within two different temperature ranges separated by a range within which a different form is stable. The lattice parameters of alpha- and delta-iron are closely similar, and the difference can be accounted for by normal thermal expansion which always causes such an increase in the size of the unit cell. The lattice parameters of cerium in the two different temperature ranges are appreciably different (see below). As has been pointed out above, it is also surprising to find a body-centred cubic structure as the low temperature stable form. The generalized discussion of the relative energy content of this form compared with close-packed structures was an oversimplification, and falls down in this particular case, due to electronic effects which were ignored.

Cobalt exists as a hexagonal close-packed form at ordinary temperatures but undergoes a transformation to a cubic close-packed form above 400°, a relatively rare transition. This particular transformation is known to be martensitic, and is sluggish and does not therefore occur at a sharp well-defined temperature.

The last element in the d block to be considered on account of its allotropy is **mercury** which is unique among metals, since it is liquid at normal temperatures. It solidifies at $-39°$ C to yield the normal alpha form which has a rhombohedral unit cell. This unit cell can be derived from a face-centred cubic structure by the compression of this latter along a body diagonal (three-fold axis)† ; this results in six of the twelve atoms neighbouring a reference atom being nearer than the other six in the rhombohedral structure. It is of interest to note that the atoms which are further distant in this structure are those six which are coplanar with

† This is a structural relationship, not a mechanism of crystal formation. It is not to be regarded as a process of compression of an already close-packed lattice. The rhombohedral lattice represents the closest packing of mercury atoms which is possible within the stability range of this form; the related face-centred cubic lattice must have larger interatomic distances, and is hypothetical only.

the reference atom, whereas in the crystal structures of zinc and cadmium, the congeners of mercury, these six coplanar atoms are nearer than the remaining six above and below the plane; these crystal structures are somewhat distorted hexagonal close-packed structures, which have a ratio of c/a of about 1·9 instead of the normal 1·63.

At low temperatures, it is possible to obtain a second, beta, form of mercury by the action of pressure. This form is said to be the more thermodynamically stable at temperatures below 79° K, metastable in the temperature range 79–90° K, and to transform readily into the alpha form above 90° K. The unit cell of the beta form is body-centred tetragonal, and this unit cell also can be derived from a face-centred cubic lattice. Fig. 4.2 shows two face-centred cubes, with a body-centred tetragonal unit cell indicated (i.e. $a = b \neq c$). It is a matter of simple trigonometry to show that the ratio of the length of the unique axis to the length of one of the other axes, i.e. c/a, is $\sqrt{2} : 1$. The ratio of

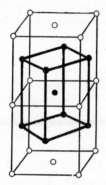

Fig. 4.2. The identity of a body-centred tetragonal lattice with face-centred cubic lattice, provided that c/a for the tetragonal cell is $\sqrt{(2)}:1$. The length c of the tetragonal unit cell (vertical direction) equals that of the cubic cell, but the length of $a = b$ of the tetragonal cell (distance two face-centres of the cubic cell) is $c/\sqrt{(2)}$.

c/a in the unit cell of beta-mercury is 0·7:1, so that it is derived from the face-centred cubic lattice by the compression of this latter along an axis of its unit cell (*cf.* the derivation of the alpha form, above).

The result of this compression is that the twelve nearest neighbours of a reference atom in the close-packed lattice cease to be equidistant from that atom when the lattice in transformed to that of beta-mercury. Each mercury atom has two nearest neighbours (which were not nearest neighbours in the original cubic lattice) arranged in a linear way parallel to the c axis, eight at a somewhat greater distance, and four at a still greater distance. It has been suggested that the transformation from one form to the other is martensitic, but the evidence is incomplete.

THE f BLOCK ELEMENTS

Although, in general, it is not possible at the present state of electronic theory to predict the crystal structure of a given metal, it is obvious that some connection between electronic configuration and structure exists, since in the *s* and *d* blocks already considered there are clear structural similarities in vertical groups of elements which have the same electronic configuration in their outer shells. Those elements in which electrons are filling an *f* level fall into two distinct groups, (i) the lanthanide, or rare earth elements and (ii) uranium and the transuranium elements*, accord-

Table 4.1. Lanthanide Structures and Transformations

Element	Transformation†	Transformation temperature, °C	Melting point, °C	Axial ratio,‡ c/a
Scandium	1–(?)	1335	1540	1·59
Yttrium	1–2	1495	1530	1·57
Lanthanum	3–4	310	920	1·61
	4–2	865	—	—
Cerium	4–2	730	800	1·62
Praseodymium	3–2	795	935	1·61
Neodymium	3–2	860	1025	1·61
Promethium	—	—	—	—
Samarium	R–2	915	1070	1·61
Europium	2	—	825	—
Gadolinium	1–(?)	1265	1310	1·59
Terbium	1–(?)	1315	1360	1·58
Dysprosium	1	—	1410	1·57
Holmium	1	—	1460	1·57
Erbium	1	—	1500	1·57
Thulium	1	—	1545	1·57
Ytterbium	4–2	800	825	—
Lutecium	1	—	1650	1·58
Actinium	4	—	1050	—

† The various structures are designated as follows:
1 = hexagonal close-packing;
2 = body-centred cubic;
3 = double hexagonal close-packing;
4 = face-centred cubic (cubic close-packing);
R = rhombohedral.
‡ These values are for the hexagonal unit cell, but with corrections applied to the double hexagonal and rhombohedral cells to allow direct comparison.

ing as the 4*f* or 5*f* shell is being occupied. It is well known that these two groups of elements are conveniently considered together because of the similarity in chemical behaviour which can be attributed to the entry of the *f* electrons into an inner quantum shell; the structural nature of the elements is no exception to this similarity, and accordingly it is convenient to treat the elements in this block under these two subdivisions. This affords further evidence of the correlation between electronic configuration and metallic structure.

* Actinium and thorium are treated with their vertical congeners.

(*i*) *The Lanthanide Elements* (including Sc, etc.). It is no longer necessary to point out that these elements are not as rare as when the term 'rare earth' was first applied to them. Pure specimens of the elements were, however, particularly rare because of the difficulties encountered for so many years in separating such chemically similar materials. They are by no means abundant at the present day, even now that modern techniques, particularly ion-exchange, have made separations a much easier task. In consequence there is not always agreement on the data of transformations, and recent papers have shown the profound effect of additives on the transformations of cerium. The data quoted in this section are those given by Spedding and Daane, and these are listed in Table 4.1.

Table 4.1 shows that many of the lanthanide elements possess a hexagonal close-packed lattice at normal temperatures, while a significant number have the double hexagonal form, which is not found for any element in the *s* or *d* block of the Periodic Table. In addition, a significant number undergo a transformation to body-centred cubic form at a temperature near the melting point. There is a number of exceptions to the general pattern, notably cerium, samarium, europium and ytterbium, and it is probably significant that these are elements which form compounds in oxidation states other than the characteristic + 3 state.

Lanthanum is unusual since it has two transformations above normal temperature. In the first of these it passes from one form of close-packing, double hexagonal, to another, cubic; the second transformation yields the normal high temperature form, i.e. body-centred cubic.

The lanthanide element most studied because of its allotropy is **cerium**. It is unique among these elements in that it has been shown to undergo transformations at very low temperatures (not listed in the Table) in addition to the high temperature transformation to the body-centred cubic form. Under normal conditions cerium possesses a cubic close-packed lattice, and differs from other elements in this group in this respect (actinium also possesses this structure). If cerium is cooled very slowly, a transformation to a new form is observed at a temperature not far below 0° C, and at a still lower temperature transformation to a further form is observed. There is not uniformity in the nomenclature of these forms, but it seems reasonable to refer to the lowest temperature form as alpha, when the normal temperature form becomes gamma, and the high-temperature body-centred cubic form becomes the delta form.

If the cooling of cerium is more rapid the gamma can transform directly into the alpha form, but at a lower temperature than that observed for the gamma–beta transition. The temperatures at which these transformations have been observed to start, whether on heating or cooling, are shown below†:

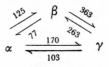

As would be expected of reactions at such low temperatures, none of these transformations proceeds rapidly, but those transformations which involve the beta phase are slower than that which does not. This observation can be understood more easily by a consideration of the structures of the various forms; the alpha form, like the gamma form, is face-

E

5d

4f

1·7   1·8 → interatomic distance (Å)
α   γ

Fig. 4.3. Possible variation in overlap of energy bands plotted against interatomic distance, for cerium.

centred cubic, whereas the beta form possesses a double hexagonal close-packed lattice. Hence the beta–alpha and beta–gamma transformations involve more drastic structural change than the alpha–gamma. It might be thought that the alpha and gamma forms are indeed identical (*cf.* iron, p. 75), and that there should be no such transformation. The unit cells are, however, very different in size. To allow a direct comparison of these at the same temperature, a sample of the gamma form was chilled extremely rapidly so that the transformation could be observed at liquid air temperature, and a single X-ray photograph was obtained with reflections due to both forms at the same temperature, i.e. while the transformation was taking place. The length of the unit cell of the gamma form is 5·14 Å, compared with a value of 4·82 Å for the alpha form and this corresponds to a 17·5% decrease in volume at that

† Temperatures are expressed on the absolute scale.

temperature, the lower temperature form being the more dense and the more compact.

It can be calculated easily that for a face-centred cubic lattice, the effective atomic radius of the element is $\sqrt{2} . a/4$, where a is the unit cell dimension. The change in the effective atomic radius of cerium in these two forms is thus from 1·82 Å to 1·70 Å. Such a change in effective atomic radius is attributed to a difference in the electronic state of the atom in the two structures. When atomic energy levels combine to form energy bands in a compact metal (Fig. 2.14 (*b*)) the extent of overlap is a function of the interatomic separation; the closer the approach of the atoms the greater the overlap of the energy bands. This is shown

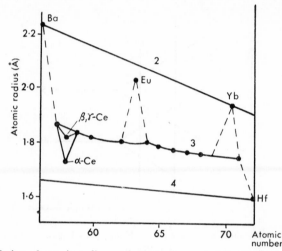

FIG. 4.4. Variation of atomic radius against atomic number in the lanthanide elements. (Ba and Hf are included for comparison.)

diagrammatically in Fig. 4.3, where it can be seen that the closer approach of the atoms in the alpha form of cerium allows a greater overlap in that structure of the energy bands derived from the 4*f* and 5*d* atomic levels. It has been calculated that the change from the gamma to the alpha form is accompanied by the transfer of half an electron per atom from the 4*f* to the 5*d* band. (The gamma form is regarded as having 3·1 electrons in the conduction band, and the alpha form 3·6.) The two forms differ in various physical properties, e.g. electrical conductivity as a result of this change.

When the effective atomic radii for the remaining lanthanide elements are also calculated and plotted against atomic number, Fig. 4.4 is obtained. It is seen that there are three roughly parallel lines in the Figure, which indicate the atomic radii expected for atoms of the

80

appropriate atomic number according to whether they contribute two, three or four electrons as valence electrons. Europium and ytterbium, two of the elements whose behaviour is untypical of the lanthanides, show behaviour which resembles the alkaline earth (divalent) elements, and their structures under normal conditions reflect this similarity, since they, like those of the alkaline earths, are cubic. The behaviour of cerium is also seen to be untypical. These three elements also have melting points below the normal range of values for the lanthanides (Table 4.1). The unique structure of samarium is not as remarkable as it might appear at first sight, since it is a distorted double-hexagonal structure, and is therefore not very different from the structures of its neighbours. The element does not occupy an anomalous position in the plot of atomic radius against atomic number.

It is significant that the lanthanides which have the electronic configuration $f > 7$ resemble each other structurally more closely than they resemble the group with configuration $f < 7$, in that transformations are less common, and a simple hexagonal rather than a double hexagonal structure is characteristic. The two groups are often differentiated chemically since the former are less basic than the latter; it has been calculated that the magnetic dipole–dipole attractions in the former elements are greater than in the lighter lanthanides, and that this may account for the structural differences of the two groups. It is significant that the values of c/a are further from the optimum value of $1·633$ than the values for the lighter lanthanides (see Table 4.1), i.e. the close-packed layers are packed more closely together than would be expected if the atoms behave as perfect spheres which have no interaction with each other.

(ii) Uranium and the Trans-uranium Elements. In this group of elements, it is impossible to obtain a completely pure specimen for study for two reasons. First, each element other than uranium must be prepared by synthesis from a second chemically similar element from which a careful separation is necessary. Secondly, every isotope of this group of elements is radioactive, and each radioactive decay process produces an impurity atom. The possible decay processes include α and β particle emission and spontaneous fission, so that a wide range of daughter products can be obtained. It is clearly necessary that a sample should be studied as quickly as possible after purification to minimize the build-up of these impurity atoms. The evolution of heat which accompanies radioactivity can make calorimetric studies and the determination of transition temperatures difficult for certain nuclides.

Studies of allotropy are limited to the elements uranium, plutonium, neptunium and americium. These are completely different from elements in any of the other categories except for the existence of body-

81

centred cubic structures for the high temperature forms. Plutonium does form a face-centred cubic structure, but even this form is not as conventional as it appears since it contracts with increase in temperature! Indeed, Seaborg and Katz wrote in 1957 that 'current theories of the metallic state will require serious modification in order to account for the amazing properties of plutonium metal'.

Uranium can be obtained in three allotropic forms, related thus

$$\alpha \underset{665°}{\overset{}{\rightleftarrows}} \beta \underset{775°}{\overset{}{\rightleftarrows}} \gamma$$

The alpha form has an orthorhombic unit cell and a structure which is unique among metals. The atoms are arranged in corrugated sheets,

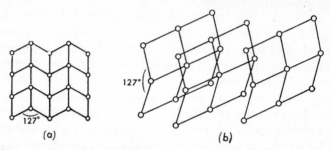

(a)   (b)

FIG. 4.5. Representation of (*a*) a buckled layer, and (*b*) the superposition of three such layers of uranium.

each of which can be regarded as a distorted close-packed layer. The necessary distortion is as shown:

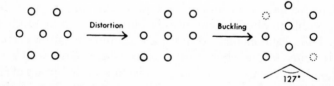

i.e. leading to a rectangular net. When such planar nets are buckled to give an angle of 'buckle' of 127° and stacked in the sequence *ABA* the structure of alpha-uranium results. This representation allows a relationship to hexagonal close-packing but the distortion is severe. Alternatively, Fig. 4.5 shows the nature of one layer, and the stacking together of layers to indicate the coordination of a given uranium atom. The immediate nearest neighbours are four atoms within a sheet, and the neighbours in the adjacent sheets are appreciably further distant. The structure can also be compared with the layer lattices of the Group V elements, although the coordination is different.

82

The beta form has a tetragonal unit cell, containing thirty atoms, and is rather complicated. The gamma form, however, is body-centred cubic. Neither the beta nor the gamma form can be preserved at ordinary temperatures if the element is pure, since the transitions occur too rapidly, but the addition of about 1% of various elements inhibits the transitions sufficiently to allow these crystal forms to be studied at room temperature in a metastable state. The alpha–beta transition is accompanied by a large volume change since the densities of the two forms are appreciably different—19·04 g/cm^3 for the alpha form compared with 18·11 g/cm^3 for the beta form. In contrast the density of the gamma form is close to that of the beta form, i.e. 18·06 g/cm^3.

Neptunium, like uranium, can be obtained in three allotropic forms, and these are represented as:

$$\alpha \underset{275°}{\overset{}{\rightleftarrows}} \beta \underset{575°}{\overset{}{\rightleftarrows}} \gamma$$

The unit cells of the three forms belong to the same systems as the analogous modifications of uranium, but with the exception of the gamma form the structures must be different as can be seen by consideration of the parameters of these unit cells, which are as follows:

		a	b	c
Alpha	U	2·85	5·87	4·96
	Np	4·72	4·89	6·66
Beta	U	10·76		5·66
	Np	4·90		3·34
Gamma	U	3·47		
	Np	3·52		

Cell lengths in Ångström units.

The densities of the three forms again show large differences and are 20·45, 19·36 and 18·00 g/cm^3 respectively.

Plutonium shows no fewer than five allotropic transformations between room temperature and its melting point at 640°, i.e. it possesses six allotropes. Four of these six forms are unique to plutonium, the remaining two being face-centred and body-centred cubic. The transition temperatures are as indicated:

$$\alpha \underset{120°}{\overset{}{\rightleftarrows}} \beta \underset{210°}{\overset{}{\rightleftarrows}} \gamma \underset{315°}{\overset{}{\rightleftarrows}} \delta \underset{460°}{\overset{}{\rightleftarrows}} \delta' \underset{475°}{\overset{}{\rightleftarrows}} \epsilon$$

A particularly elegant demonstration of the existence of the various forms is illustrated in Fig. 4.6. A sample of plutonium was allowed to rise in temperature, heated only by the effect of its own radioactivity, and the expansion measured. The plot of relative expansion (or contraction) against temperature shows breaks corresponding to each transition. It can be seen that the density changes are not uniform in

83

direction, as they are in uranium and neptunium, since the delta prime–epsilon and delta–delta prime (δ') transitions lead to the formation of denser forms and are accompanied by contraction in volume instead of expansion. It is characteristic of the unusual behaviour of this element that the transformation to the denser forms coincides with formation of structures normally regarded as less compact, since they are not based on close-packing (see below).

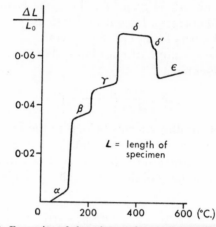

FIG. 4.5. Expansion of plutonium under conditions of self-heating (after Abramson).

Both the alpha and beta forms of plutonium are monoclinic. The detailed structure of the alpha form is known and is very complex; the unit cell contains sixteen atoms and these occupy no fewer than eight non-equivalent crystallographic sites, i.e. with different coordinations. The structure of the beta form has not yet been resolved; the unit cell contains thirty-four atoms. The gamma form is orthorhombic, and can be described as two interpenetrating face-centred orthorhombic lattices, with the origin of the second lattice corresponding to a position one-quarter of the distance along the body diagonal of the first lattice from its origin. This unusual structure has each atom in a position of irregular ten-fold coordination.

The delta form is face-centred cubic, but as has been pointed out previously, has anomalous properties for which there is no satisfactory explanation. The transformation to the delta-prime form involves a very minor structural change, but it is quite certain that this latter phase is a definite allotrope. The structure of the delta-prime form is face-centred tetragonal, in contrast to the face-centred cubic structure of the delta form. This change means that two of the axes become slightly longer and

84

the third slightly shorter as a result of the transition, the unit cells of the two forms differing in volume by only 1%. The actual dimensions are:

Delta $\quad\quad a = b = c = 4.64$ Å

Delta-prime $\quad a = b = 4.70$ Å, $\quad c = 4.46$ Å

It is not surprising, in view of the slight structural change, that the energy associated with it is very small indeed, and much less than for any of the other transitions of plutonium.

The last, epsilon, phase has the straightforward body-centred cubic structure commonly found in high temperature forms of elements. This form has the normal thermal properties, in contrast to the two previous forms. Theoretical knowledge is still a long way from an understanding of the allotropy of plutonium, and the other 5f elements. The allotropy is in character with the chemical behaviour of these elements, however, since the closeness of the various electronic energy levels leads to a wide variety of stable oxidation states. The various allotropes, doubtless, correspond to slightly different types of bonding which are possible on account of this same closeness of different energy levels.

Just as the number of stable oxidation states decreases as atomic number passes beyond that of plutonium, so the number of allotropic forms of the next element, **americium**, seems, as far as our present limited knowledge goes, to decrease also. It is believed that americium can be obtained in two forms, an alpha form which has the double hexagonal close-packed structure, found previously for the lighter lanthanide elements only, and a beta form which has a cubic close-packed structure. This is thought to be a higher temperature form, and its transformation to the hexagonal form at low temperatures has been observed. Even less is known of the elements beyond americium.

THE p BLOCK ELEMENTS

Whereas in the s, d and f blocks of the Periodic Table every element is a true metal, the p block contains both metals and non-metals, and some elements whose behaviour is intermediate and which are referred to sometimes as metalloids—these include the semi-conductors referred to in the earlier section. No discussion has been attempted of the correlation between the electronic configuration of a metallic element and the crystal structure adopted in the solid state, since it cannot be said that such correlation is fully understood. In contrast, possible structures for the elements of the p block can be more readily predicted from a consideration of their electronic configurations, by use of hybridization and localized molecular orbitals.

The elements within this block are considered, like those of the s and d blocks, in vertical groups of the Periodic Table according to their electronic configurations.

(*i*) *The Group III Elements.* The electronic configuration of elements in this group is s^2p^1 and the $(8-N)$ rule for such an element requires five nearest neighbours. Each atom has insufficient electrons to allow it to contribute one electron to an electron pair bond to each of five neighbouring atoms. Further, it is not possible to construct a regular polyhedron with five corners such that these can pack together economically in space to form an infinite three- or two-dimensional lattice where each atom has an identical environment. With the exception of boron, all the Group III elements are metallic in character and have coordinations higher than five, so that there cannot be an electron pair localized between each pair of atoms. **Boron**, however, is a non-metal and presents structural problems different from those of the remaining elements of the group. The only elements in the group which have allotropic forms are boron and thallium.

It is particularly difficult to prepare pure boron because of its very high melting point, 2300° C, and the highly corrosive behaviour of the liquid which reacts with metals to form borides very readily. Hoard and Newkirk have recently reviewed the subject of the allotropy of boron very critically. Very many different allotropic modifications have been claimed, and these authors have analysed in detail the X-ray data and concluded that there are three definite allotropic modifications, one which has not yet been proved conclusively, and various others which are doubtful or invalid.

The form which is presumed to be thermodynamically stable under normal conditions is known as the alpha rhombohedral form. This is prepared by thermal decomposition methods in the temperature range 800–1100°, e.g. the decomposition of BBr_3 on a heated metal filament. This allows the element to form crystals which grow slowly as decomposition proceeds. If this form is heated to higher temperatures it transforms to a new form, beta-rhombohedral, which is itself formed by thermal decomposition at temperatures above 1250°. The third accepted form has crystals which belong to the tetragonal system, and is named accordingly. It is obtained by the reduction of boron tribromide with hydrogen over a metal filament heated to 1300°; this is the material referred to on p. 6 as forming both needles and plates. The form not yet established, which also has tetragonal symmetry, has been obtained under apparently the same conditions, and will be referred to as tetragonal-II.

The structures of the alpha-rhombohedral and tetragonal forms have been established, but those of beta-rhombohedral and tetragonal-II which contain 108 and 192 atoms respectively in their unit cells are as yet unknown. The feature of the two known structures is that the boron atoms are arranged in B_{12} units where each unit has the form of an icosahedron, so-called because it has twenty faces, all of which are triangular in shape. An icosahedron is illustrated in Fig. 4.7; it can be described alternatively as two pentagonal (five-membered) rings superimposed one above the other, but with one ring rotated through 36° with respect to the other so that a corner of one does not lie immediately above a corner of the other—this is a pentagonal antiprism; the two remaining corners are above and below the antiprism, which can thus be said to terminate in two pentagonal pyramids.

Icosahedra of boron atoms are found in compounds of the element also, such as B_4C, so that it is of theoretical interest to obtain an understanding of this arrangement, which is not found in other elements. It is a particularly economical way to pack atoms in space, and is presumably found in boron since it has insufficient electrons to 'obey' the $(8-N)$ rule. It is necessary to use a molecular orbital treatment involving both localization and delocalization. Each of the twelve constituent atoms has one $2s$ and three $2p$ atomic orbitals, making a total of 48 orbitals for a complete icosahedron of boron atoms. It is necessary to combine

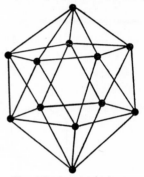

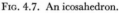

FIG. 4.7. An icosahedron.

these to form 48 molecular orbitals, and this has been done theoretically. There is one localized orbital pointing outwards from each of the atoms of the icosahedron, and thirteen bonding orbitals available for bonding within the icosahedron, the remainder being either anti-bonding or non-bonding.

The structure of tetragonal boron follows very simply from this theory. It comprises icosahedra arranged in a manner closely similar to that of cubic close-packing, so that each icosahedron has six neighbours arranged around it in one plane with three above and three below, part of the plane with six nearest neighbouring icosahedra being shown in Fig. 4.8. This plane contains six boron atoms from each icosahedron arranged as a regular hexagon. Three atoms of each icosahedron are arranged in an equilateral triangle above, and three below in a similar manner. Each atom of the two triangular sets is bonded to a similar atom in one of the six adjacent icosahedra in the planes above and below, by the overlapping of their individual localized orbitals, i.e. those which point outwards from the icosahedron. The localized orbital of each of the six equatorial atoms overlaps with two similar orbitals from separate adjacent icosahedra, which have appropriate symmetry and directional properties to form a tricentric molecular orbital. Such a tricentric orbital containing two electrons is known as a three-centre bond. Each atom must contribute $\frac{2}{3}$ of an electron to form such a bond.

Considering the electron balance of a given icosahedron, it is seen that six electron pair sigma bonds are formed from each icosahedron and use six electrons per icosahedron; six atoms contribute $\frac{2}{3}$ electron each to tricentric orbitals, i.e. four electrons per icosahedron. Thus ten electrons per icosahedron are used in bonding to other icosahedra; this leaves twenty-six electrons available for bonding within each icosahedron, and it was pointed out above that there are thirteen bonding orbitals available, so that the number of electrons exactly fills the available bonding orbitals, but none of the anti-bonding or non-bonding orbitals. Such an

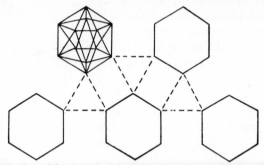

Fig. 4.8. The projection of five icosahedra of the structure of tetragonal boron—the atoms held by three-centre bonds are those joined by dashed lines.

arrangement is, as was seen in the discussion of molecular orbital theory, a very stable one. It is worthy of note that the B—B distances within the icosahedron and when bonded by bicentric bonds are approximately 1·7 Å, whereas the distance between two boron atoms of the tricentric bond is about 15% greater, i.e. two electrons can hold two atoms closer than they can hold three.

It is less easy to explain completely the structure of the low temperature alpha rhombohedral form. The unit cell contains two isolated boron atoms in addition to four complete icosahedra, i.e. 50 atoms per cell. Each isolated atom is surrounded tetrahedrally by four icosahedra and is bonded to one atom in each of its four neighbouring polyhedra. Whereas the detailed theory is difficult, the existence of the B_{12} units is significant. It may be that the two unsolved structures contain only icosahedra, since the number of atoms in each unit cell is divisible by twelve.

There is little information concerning transformations from one form to another, except the observation that the alpha-rhombohedral form has been found to transform to the beta-rhombohedral form on heating. The remaining forms could be monotropes, and indeed Hoard and

Newkirk believe that any other genuine forms must also be monotropic. These have commonly been obtained under particular conditions by thermal methods using different temperatures and different substrates on which the boron is deposited, and are known to have different X-ray powder patterns.

To explain the various incompletely characterized materials which have been claimed as allotropes of boron, but which in some cases at least have been prepared only by one team of workers, Hoard and Newkirk argue from the extreme reactivity of hot boron, and the ease with which it forms binary borides of varying stoicheiometries with most other elements. They suggest, and the idea is worthy of serious consideration, perhaps not for boron only, that the initial deposit of boron reacts with the substrate to form metal boride, with appropriate crystal lattice, and once that structural pattern has been determined it continues in the subsequently deposited boron. If the crystal grows more rapidly than the attacked metal atoms can diffuse outwards, the metal content of the crystals decreases steadily with distance from the substrate, and a sample can be detached and analysed which contains virtually no metal at all. The structure is still that determined by the initial metal boride phase, and these phases are very varied both in structure and stoicheiometry. Even although the material analyses as pure boron, it is really a limiting case of a non-stoicheiometric metal boride, containing an undetectable proportion of the metal.

If these ideas are correct, such products are not really allotropes, and it could be that one or more of the accepted allotropes might be invalidated by the same arguments.

To conclude the section on Group III elements, it can be said that aluminium, gallium and indium are obtainable in one solid form only (not isostructural), but **thallium** exists in two allotropic forms. The low temperature form is hexagonally close-packed, but on heating undergoes a transition at 230° C to give a body-centred cubic high temperature form.

(*ii*) *The Group IV Elements.* The outer electronic configuration of elements in this group is $s^2 p^2$ and the $(8-N)$ rule requires that an atom of a Group IV element should have four nearest neighbours. Hence the formation of a sigma bond with each of its four valence electrons results, by electron pairing, in the atom having complete s and p levels. There are two symmetrical ways in which an atom can form four equivalent bonds, i.e. directed to the corners of a square, or to the corners of a regular tetrahedron. In the former arrangement the bonds are coplanar and the bonding electron pairs are at 90° to each other, whereas in the latter the distribution of the bonds is three-dimensional and the electron pairs are at 109° 28' to each other. This larger angle would be expected to minimize the repulsion forces (Fig. 2.1) and yield a more stable structure.

Moreover, by hybridization of s and p orbitals it is possible to obtain four equivalent hybrid atomic orbitals which point to the corners of a regular tetrahedron but it is not possible to obtain hybrid orbitals directed to the corners of a square from such orbitals.

Group IV shows the trend in behaviour, referred to on p. 51, that the lightest element is a non-metal (insulator), the heaviest a metal (conductor), with metalloids (semi-conductors) intermediate. Only two of the elements can be obtained in different allotropic modifications—carbon and tin.

Carbon can be obtained in three different crystalline modifications, alpha- and beta-graphite, and diamond, and in various amorphous forms such as soot, carbon black, etc. These amorphous materials contain very small particles with a graphite-like structure but have a very large surface area with impurity atoms on the surface, so are really impure graphite. This point will be considered further in connection with the structures of the graphites (p. 93). Diamond is characterized by its extreme hardness which results in its use as an abrasive, and the high polish which it takes makes it a valuable gemstone. The density of diamond is $3 \cdot 51$ g/cm^3 compared with the value of $2 \cdot 22$ g/cm^3 of graphite. Graphite is characterized by its softness, the ease with which it forms flakes, and hence finds use as a lubricant; it has black colour and opacity in contrast to the colourless transparence of diamond. Graphite is more reactive chemically than diamond, e.g. it is ignited to form carbon dioxide at a lower temperature, and is able to conduct electricity whereas diamond is an insulator.

The structures of diamond and graphite have been referred to previously (p. 65 *et seq.* and p. 51); diamond is the analogue of aliphatic compounds since it is based on a tetrahedral distribution of bonds from each carbon atom (as expected from the $8 - N$ rule), whereas graphite is the analogue of aromatic compounds with a trigonal planar distribution of bonds from each atom. The carbon–carbon bond in the structure of diamond has a length of $1 \cdot 54$ Å, and is a pure single (sigma) bond. The hardness of diamond is attributed to the high energy required to break the C—C bond, i.e. the amount of energy given out when two carbon atoms come together with overlap of orbitals, or the stabilization energy of the two bonded atoms with respect to two isolated atoms; on account of the high (cubic) symmetry of the structure, any section through the crystal encounters equally large numbers of chemical bonds which are difficult to break, so that no directions of easy cleavage exist. The development of crystal faces which can reflect light and make diamond a valuable gemstone is facilitated by the high symmetry of the structure, and the lack of colour is attributed to a large gap (approx. 4 eV) between a full electronic band and the vacant band of next higher energy.

90

The structure of alpha-graphite is illustrated in Fig. 4.9. The distance between carbon atoms within a plane is 1·41 Å, whereas the planes are 3·35 Å apart. The shortening of the bond from 1·54 to 1·41 Å is attributed to the pi bonding as described on p. 51; whereas two atoms in diamond are held together by two electrons, in graphite they are held by $2\frac{2}{3}$ electrons. The greater distance between the layers indicates that the bonding between layers is very weak, since no electrons are available to form bonds between them. Thus the packing of atoms in graphite is much less compact than in diamond, and this accounts for the lower density of graphite. The weakness of the bonding between adjacent layers of carbon atoms allows a crystal of graphite to be cleaved particularly in this direction and accounts for the softness of the material, and the different interatomic distances result in

a different electronic band structure from diamond; graphite has overlapping bands which enable it to have a weak, but definite, conductivity and optical properties like those of metals.

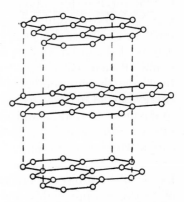

FIG. 4.9. The structure of alpha-graphite—the sequence of stacking of the layers of six-membered rings is *ABA*.

The conductivity of graphite decreases with increase in temperature which is the characteristic of metallic conduction in contrast to semi-conduction. It has been calculated that at room temperature there are 10^{-4}–10^{-5} electrons per atom in the upper, conduction, band. It is possible to visualize the electrical conductivity of graphite since, as was seen previously, the p_z atomic orbitals overlap to give a completely delocalized system of molecular orbitals, thus permitting electron transport throughout an entire crystal. The presence of impurity atoms can change the band structure of graphite, or any other material, and hence change its conduction properties.

It is strictly inaccurate to refer to graphite without qualification, since it is now known that there are two forms of graphite, designated alpha and beta. These are identical in their physical properties except for their crystal structure, so that the foregoing discussion applies to both forms equally. Whereas the layers of carbon atoms in alpha-graphite, which was illustrated, are arranged in the sequence *ABABABA*, reminiscent of hexagonal close-packing of metals, those of beta-graphite are arranged in the sequence *ABCABCABCA*, reminiscent of cubic close-packing. The unit cells of the two materials have hexagonal and rhombohedral symmetry respectively. Some naturally occurring graphites

91

have been reported to contain as much as 30% of the rhombohedral (beta) form, whereas synthetic materials contain only the alpha form. The alpha form can be largely converted to the beta form by mechanical treatment (*cf.* the cold-working of metals such as lithium and sodium), but the beta form reverts to the alpha form on heating to above 1000° C. The transition between the two forms can be compared with that between cubic and hexagonal close-packed metals, but is not completely analogous, since the nature of the bonding in the two cases is different.

In view of the high value of diamonds and the cheapness and ready availability of graphite, it is not surprising that the transformation from one to the other has been studied extensively. The two crystal structures have different primary coordination, and different chemical bonding, so that the transformation is of a reconstructive nature and would be expected to occur only sluggishly. Graphite is the thermodynamically more stable form, though the energy difference between the two forms is only of the order of 500 cal/g-atom. The change of structure is profound (though each form contains networks of six-membered rings, buckled in diamond and planar in graphite), and results in a considerable energy barrier to be overcome during the transition; hence the transition to the more thermodynamically stable form, graphite, is extremely slow under normal conditions. Some naturally occurring diamonds have a surface coating of graphite.

The transformation in the reverse direction is the more attractive and has been the subject of much research. Since it involves the formation of a form of appreciably higher density, the transformation is accompanied by an appreciable decrease in volume, and is therefore favoured by an increase in pressure. The equation for the transition curve, which defines the conditions under which both forms are in equilibrium, has been found to be:

$$P = 7100 + 27T$$

where P is the pressure in atmospheres, and T is the temperature in degrees Kelvin. Thus, at room temperature, a pressure of about 15,000 atmospheres would be required before the transition of graphite to diamond could occur. Within the last decade efforts to prepare synthetic diamonds were at last successful. Graphite was heated to temperatures in the range 1300–1800° C, and it can be calculated from the above expression that at these temperatures pressures in the range from 50,000–70,000 atmospheres are required. It is usual to add a catalyst such as a transition metal, and it is considered that this can facilitate reaction by acting as a solvent for carbon under these extreme conditions. It was noted on p. 23 that such solvent action facilitates the mechanism of transformation. Diamonds have also been obtained by the use of shock

92

waves, which produce high pressures momentarily. As yet those diamonds which have been prepared synthetically have been very small, and have some slight differences from natural diamonds. The origin of natural diamonds is a matter of considerable theoretical interest.

Reference was made above to the difference in chemical reactivity of diamond and graphite; the excess of energy possessed by diamond results in a greater heat of reaction when this form of the element combines with another element, than when graphite so combines. Graphite reacts faster than diamond because of the large surface area of the laminae, and the availability of pi electrons in the easily accessible reaction sites between the laminae. An important chemical difference between the two forms is the ability of graphite to form intercalation compounds, as a consequence of its particular structure, often on mere exposure to the vapours of various elements and compounds.

There are two types of such compounds, in the first of which the electrical conductivity and black colour of the graphite are lost whereas in the second the conductivity is increased and the resulting compound is often strongly coloured. A compound of the first type is obtained when graphite is exposed to fluorine under appropriate conditions. The stoicheiometry of the product formed, which is colourless and an insulator is not the conventional CF_4, but rather CF, carbon monofluoride. The fluorine atoms are intercalated between the sheets of carbon atoms so that one is bonded to each; each carbon atom is then bonded to three other carbon atoms within the same sheet, as before reaction with fluorine, and to a fluorine atom additionally. To allow this, the carbon atom must use not sp^2 hybrid orbitals, but sp^3, with a consequent change in bond angle, which buckles the sheets and pushes them farther apart than in the uncombined graphite.

The other well-known compound of this type is the so-called graphitic oxide formed by chemical oxidation in an aqueous system. The structure of this material is not fully understood, and is complex, but it is certain that oxygen atoms are between buckled graphitic layers. In addition to oxygen, graphitic oxide contains some hydrogen and there is evidence that the structure contains $COOH$ and OH groups, in addition to ether linkages. The surface layer of the amorphous forms of carbon doubtless contains oxygen, etc., bonded in a manner similar to graphitic oxide.

There are more examples known of the second type of compound in which the conductivity of the parent graphite is retained. It is possible to isolate materials of varying stoicheiometries for a given system, i.e. the value of m in the formula C_mR, where the intercalated species represented by R, is not constant. Some examples of components R with the minimum attainable value of m are as follows: $HfCl_4$ (1310); MoO_3 (99); FeS_2 (72); CrO_2Cl_2 (16); Cl_2 (16); $FeCl_3$ (8); K (8).

The atoms or molecules of R lie in ordered positions in layers between the layers of carbon atoms, and it appears that such an intercalated layer is completed before a second such layer starts to form. If the value of m for a particular preparation is greater than the minimum possible, the sequence of layers may be ordered or random according to experimental conditions. The stacking of the graphite layers is altered somewhat when such a compound is formed, so that two layers of carbon atoms which sandwich a layer of R are directly one above the other. Two examples which illustrate this for different uptakes of R are:

$$ABABABA \text{ (graphite)} \longrightarrow ABRBARA \longrightarrow ARARARA$$

If an intercalation compound is prepared from rhombohedral graphite, and then decomposed by heating, the intercalated species R is driven off, and the graphite regenerated in the more stable hexagonal form. The compound formation modifies the positions of the graphitic layers, and when the compound is broken down the layers assume the more stable sequence rather than the original. This can be compared with the mechanism of transformation involving a vapour phase or solution intermediate.

When these compounds are formed it is likely that some transference of electrons takes place either from the pi cloud of the graphite to the intercalated species, or in the reverse direction. In the former situation vacancies are created at the top of the normally full band, whereas in the latter situation electrons are added to the conduction band of the graphite. The electrical conductivity is thus retained, and may even be enhanced by such compound formation; the compounds can absorb light and are coloured.

The structure of diamond is adopted both by silicon and germanium, which have no alternative allotropic forms, whereas the heaviest member of the group, lead, has a cubic close-packed structure.

Tin can exist in two forms, one of which behaves as a semiconductor and the other as a metal with good metallic conduction. The low temperature form of tin, known as grey tin, has the same structure as diamond. Each atom thus has four nearest neighbours at a distance of 2·80 Å, and the density of this form is 5·77 g/cm³. It has been pointed out previously that the approach to metallic character as atomic number increases within a group results from the closer approach of corresponding energy levels, and bands, as the principal quantum number of the electrons increases; this can be illustrated by the values of the energy gaps in the four elements in this Group all of which crystallize with the same, diamond, structure. These gaps are as follows: carbon, 4·0 eV; silicon, 1·12; germanium, 0·67; tin, 0·08. Hence, only a very small gap has to be overcome by an electron in grey tin to allow it to enter the conduction band.

94

The high temperature form of tin has a less regular structure, and its unit cell is shown in Fig. 4.10. It is tetragonal, with an atom at the body centre and atoms situated one-quarter of a unit cell dimension above or below four of the six face centres as shown. This gives each atom six coordination in an irregular way so that the four nearest neighbours, joined to the reference atom in the Figure by dotted and dashed lines, are disposed towards the corners of a flattened tetrahedron, while the remaining two neighbours are slightly farther distant and collinear with the reference atom. It could also be described as an octahedron with the equatorial plane distorted. The interatomic distances are 3·02 and 3·18 Å respectively, and are thus appreciably greater than those in grey tin. The density of the white form is 7·29 g/cm³.

The transition temperature at which the two forms can be maintained in equilibrium is 13·2° C. The two forms differ in their primary coordination, and apparently in the nature of their bonding, so that, as in the case

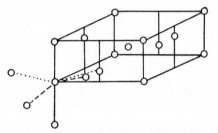

FIG. 4.10. The structure of grey (tetragonal) tin. The six-fold coordination of one atom is shown.

of carbon, the transition would be expected to be sluggish. It is not, however, as difficult to observe as the diamond–graphite transition; the difference in energy between the two forms is comparable in magnitude with that between the two forms of carbon, but presumably the energy barrier is not as high. The large difference in density of the two forms results in a considerable contraction in volume in the transition from grey to white tin, and a similar increase in the reverse direction. It is not possible to observe this change in one crystal and investigate the relative orientations of the two forms before and after the transition, since a crystal of one form falls to pieces as the transformation occurs.

The form of tin which is used for metallurgical purposes is the metallic white, or high temperature form, and since this crumbles if it undergoes the transformation at 13·2° C it is fortunate that the change is such a slow one. The rate of transformation increases as the temperature drops significantly below the transition temperature, but decreases again at still lower temperatures. The story of the buttons on the overcoats of Napoleon's soldiers falling off on account of the extreme cold during the retreat from Moscow illustrates this point. A similar, if less often told story, is that Scott was deprived of fuel and food on his return from the South Pole since the solder on the fuel cans contained too much tin, and could not stand the low temperatures, so that the fuel oil leaked and ruined the food. Whatever the truth of the stories, they make a valid chemical point.

The difference in the interatomic distances observed in the two different forms is consistent with different band structures (*cf.* the two forms of cerium and Fig. 4.3).

(*iii*) *The Group V Elements.* The electronic configuration of elements in this group is $s^2 p^3$, and the $(8 - N)$ rule requires that an atom of a Group V element should have three nearest neighbours. The formation of three sigma bonds to such nearest neighbours gives the atom complete s and p levels, and there is a non-bonding (or lone) pair of electrons associated with each atom in addition to the three bonding pairs.

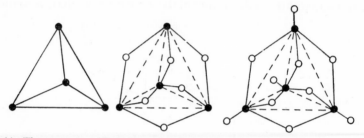

Fig. 4.11. The structures of P_4, P_4O_6, and P_4O_{10} showing the preservation of the tetrahedral unit, but the expansion of the interbond angle from 60° to 109° 28'.

A manner in which each atom can be bonded to three other atoms with the formation of an infinite structure is by a trigonal distribution of bonds, as in the structure of graphite. This structure is possible for carbon, since when each atom uses sp^2 hybrid orbitals, a single electron remains in the p_z orbital, and all these orbitals can overlap to form a pi system. The Group V elements possess one additional electron, so that each p_z orbital would be full and hence unable to bond with its neighbours. Alternatively, since all four valence orbitals are completely occupied after three sigma bonds are formed, a Group V element can use sp^3 hybrid orbitals to form a buckled sheet such as has been described in the structure of carbon monofluoride. This preserves the essential trigonal pattern, but without the planarity of the graphite structure, the fourth non-bonding pair of electrons occupying the fourth tetrahedral position, and pointing away from the three sigma bonds within the buckled sheet. Such a sheet contains six-membered rings as in diamond rather than in graphite, and these have been illustrated in Figs. 3.10, 3.11, 3.12, and 3.13.

Some forms of the Group V elements, however, possess the properties associated with small molecules rather than with polymeric structures (see p. 62). There are two ways in which such a small molecule can be envisaged. First, if the three atoms held by bonds emanating from a given atom are 'tied together' by further bonds then a tetrahedral molecule results (see Fig. 4.11). Secondly, for an atom of the first short period, there is the possibility of $p\pi$—$p\pi$ overlap, and the diatomic molecule of nitrogen where the two atoms are held together by one sigma and two pi bonds has already been described (p. 41).

Nitrogen, being gaseous under normal conditions, has the physical properties characteristic of a small molecule, and it is well known that it forms a diatomic molecule. The small size of the nitrogen atom compared with the later members of Group V results in appreciable bond stabilization by pi overlap so that the diatomic molecule has a low internal energy. The atoms would require to be further apart, possible only if the element were at a high temperature, for formation of three sigma bonds per nitrogen atom instead of one sigma and two pi bonds, so that it is highly unlikely that any other molecular form could exist. The increase in temperature (input of energy) eventually breaks the bond and forms the monatomic species at very high temperatures. There are two allotropes of nitrogen known in the solid state, but each crystal structure comprises diatomic molecules. The change from one form to the other involves the secondary coordination only, so that the transition takes place rapidly; the difference in the energy of the two forms is very small, viz. 54 cal/g-mol. The transition and stability ranges of the two forms are as indicated:

$$\alpha \underset{36°K}{\overset{\longrightarrow}{\rightleftharpoons}} \beta \underset{63°K}{\overset{\longrightarrow}{\rightleftharpoons}} \text{Liquid}$$

A brief discussion of the so-called active nitrogen is included in the final Chapter, pp. 124–125.

Phosphorus and its neighbour sulphur are those elements for which the largest number of different allotropic forms have been claimed. It is doubtful, however, if all these claims are valid. The toxic nature of phosphorus, and the inflammability of the white form, give rise to some experimental difficulty and hazard, which accounts for some incompleteness in experimental evidence concerning the behaviour of such a common element.

The element is prepared normally by the carbothermic reduction of phosphorus (V) oxide, and condenses from the vapour phase, in which it is formed, as the so-called white (or, alternatively, yellow) phosphorus. It is more correct to call it alpha-white phosphorus, since a second white form, known as the beta form, can be obtained from it by an enantio-

97

tropic change at $-77°$ C. The melting point of alpha-white phosphorus is $44°$ C and the boiling point $280°$, and these low temperatures are appropriate for a small molecule. In accordance with this, the material is soluble in non-polar covalently bonded solvents. The main characteristic of this form of phosphorus is its high reactivity towards other elements, and, in particular, oxygen, so that it is normally stored under water, with which it does not react. It inflames spontaneously in air at a temperature above its melting point, and the glow which it emits in the dark, phosphorescence, is caused by the oxidation of its vapour, which is a slow process on account of the low vapour pressure of the solid.

Whereas the unit cell dimensions of white phosphorus have been reported, it appears that no complete structural analysis has yet been carried out. The vapour with which it is in equilibrium has been shown to be composed of P_4 molecules, and molecular weight determinations using solutions of white phosphorus in non-polar solvents from which the material can be recrystallized unchanged also indicate a P_4 unit. There is no doubt that solid white phosphorus comprises P_4 tetrahedra (Fig. 4.11) with dimensions not appreciably different from those of the vapour phase molecule, i.e. an interbond angle of $60°$ and a bond length of $2·21$ Å. The molecule affords each phosphorus atom the three co-ordination expected for a Group V element; the bond length is close to that assigned for a pure sigma bond P—P ($2·20$ Å), but the bond angle is much less than the tetrahedral angle expected if sp^3 hybrid orbitals are used, or than the right angle if pure p orbitals are used. Such a low valence angle is extremely rare, with cyclopropane as perhaps the only other known example. In consequence the overlap of the atomic orbitals must be less than if a more normal inter-bond angle existed in the molecule, and it may be significant that the bond length is slightly longer than a normal single bond, although experimental error makes this point uncertain.

The less complete overlap results in less energy being given out when the molecule is formed than would be expected if the more complete overlap present in other forms of the element occurred. Thus the molecule has a higher internal energy than might be expected, and this, sometimes known as the strain energy, is given out in chemical reactions which result in the phosphorus atoms forming more normal bond angles. This energy has been evaluated as 23 kcal/g-mol of P_4; it is not available for other forms of phosphorus which are accordingly less reactive. The oxidation of phosphorus to form P_4O_6 and P_4O_{10} illustrates the increase in bond angle, and as was seen above, takes place readily (see Fig. 4.11).

The existence of a form of high internal energy under normal conditions, i.e. room temperature and atmospheric pressure, at which it is

98

metastable, is due entirely to the method of preparation, in which it is chilled rapidly from a high temperature so that it does not have time to change to a more stable form, and to a high energy barrier which separates it from more stable forms. Brown phosphorus and purple sulphur, to be described below, are further similar examples.

If white phosphorus is maintained at a temperature just below its boiling point for some time, or is subjected to irradiation, e.g. by X-rays, it gradually develops a red colour. The process can be catalysed by the addition of materials such as iodine. The properties reported for the red form of phosphorus seem to be somewhat variable, even after the material has been freed carefully from unchanged white phosphorus, and the catalytic preparations have been shown to contain atoms of the catalyst incorporated in the lattice. It is at best poorly crystalline. The density is $2 \cdot 3$ g/cm^3 compared with $1 \cdot 83$ g/cm^3 for the white form, and the melting point is about 590° compared with 44°; the red form is insoluble, and hence polymeric, and has a very low vapour pressure, although the vapour contains P_4 tetrahedra. It is comparatively non-toxic, and less reactive than the white form, and hence can be stored much more easily. The structural nature of this material will be considered along with that of the other forms of the element.

Hittorf discovered that crystallization of phosphorus from molten lead or bismuth yielded violet crystals with similar properties to red phosphorus, except for rates of reaction. This material contains at least traces of metal, and is not pure phosphorus. It has been suggested further that the difference between the two materials is caused by particle size. It was found that when a suspension of red phosphorus was oxidized in aqueous medium the colour of the unoxidized material gradually changed from red to violet-black, suggesting that the smaller particles were oxidized first, and this is in accord with the suggestion that there is little difference between red and violet phosphorus.

Bridgman subjected white phosphorus to a pressure of 1200 atmospheres at a temperature of 220° for some time and obtained a black form of the element. Modifications of the experimental procedure have yielded amorphous black and vitreous materials, and recently Krebs and his co-workers obtained black phosphorus without the use of elevated pressures by heating the white form for 5 days at 380° C in the presence of liquid mercury. These various products are not identical in properties. The Bridgman black phosphorus has a density of $2 \cdot 7$ g/cm^3 and is the most dense form of the element. It has the appearance of graphite, and at normal pressures behaves as a semiconductor with the relatively small energy gap of $0 \cdot 3$ eV (the gap of red phosphorus is about $1 \cdot 5$ eV); at high pressures it shows metallic conductivity. It is insoluble, and is less reactive chemically than the other forms, e.g. it inflames with oxygen only at

99

about 400°, compared with a corresponding temperature of 250° for the red form. When maintained at 540° for some time, the black form passes into the red form.

The structure of black phosphorus has been described in some detail on p. 67, and Figs. 3.12, 3.13, where it can be seen that each phosphorus atom is bonded to three other neighbours within a buckled sheet. The bond length observed is 2·18Å, which is significantly shorter than the bond length in the white modification, but the bond angle is 102° which does not involve any strain in the structure. As suggested in Chapter 2, this angle is obtained by the hybridization of one s and three p orbitals to give non-equivalent orbitals, so that those used in bonding in black phosphorus have rather more p character than equivalent sp^3 hybrids, and the lone pair is accommodated in an orbital which has rather more s character. The distance between a phosphorus atom in one layer and its nearest neighbour in the next layer is 3·68 Å, so that, as in graphite, there is no strong force holding adjacent layers together. The relationship of this structure to that of sodium chloride has been pointed out in Chapter 3.

The monomeric structure of white phosphorus and the polymeric structure of black phosphorus are thus well established, and it is clear from the physical properties of the remaining forms which have been mentioned, that they are closer to the black than to the white form. The remaining forms do not give sharp X-ray diffraction patterns and structural information is obtainable only from radial distribution curves, whence it is clear that a coordination number of three at a distance of approximately 2·20 Å is a common feature. Differences in the various structures are apparent at longer ranges.

It is useful at this point to consider the transformation from white to black phosphorus. Although three-coordination is common to both forms, consideration of the structures, as they have been described above, indicates that profound reconstruction must accompany the change. When one bond of a P_4 tetrahedron is broken, some strain is relieved, and a fragment with free radical character such as that shown below, results.

The function of a catalyst is obviously to provide an element with which phosphorus can react, since such reaction opens up the P_4 tetrahedron and breaks a P—P bond. Such a fragment as the above can link with other similar fragments to form a chain, and if the bridge bonds in such fragments also break, cross-linking of the chains to form a sheet with its fused six-membered ring structure will result. The continuation of such a process in the solid state must involve the movement of increasingly large fragments, which must be able to orient themselves appropriately. Such a process must involve large energy barriers, so that the application both of heat and pressure is necessary to form the most stable and compact form. Perhaps the mercury in Krebs' preparation acts as a solvent, and thus facilitates reaction.

It seems most logical to conclude that the various other forms of phosphorus—red, violet, amorphous black, vitreous, etc.—represent intermediate stages in the polymerization and that the precise structural arrangement of any given material will depend upon the exact conditions under which it was prepared. No such material can give a definite X-ray pattern, because there will be no long range order in a structure which consists of a tangle of chains, cross-linked at various points, and of rings which can join together in *cis* or *trans* conformations when the conditions of the experiment are of non-equilibrium.

If this conclusion is accepted, none of these materials constitutes a definite allotropic form, since none is structurally homogeneous, and it is probable that none can be exactly reproduced. None the less, whether it is a definite allotrope or not, it is clear that there is a material which can be described as red phosphorus.

The transformation from alpha-white to beta-white phosphorus is a simple enantiotropic one, which presumably involves only a slight rearrangement of the tetrahedra with respect to one another, involving secondary coordination only, so that it takes place rapidly and reversibly. The normal alpha form belongs to the cubic system, whereas the low temperature beta form has a hexagonal unit cell.

It is now accepted that the black form of phosphorus is the most thermodynamically stable form, and various data are available to substantiate this. Values of ΔH for the various changes are shown below.

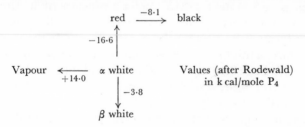

A molecule P_2, the analogue of diatomic nitrogen, can be obtained in the gas phase at high temperature, at which the P_4 molecule finally dissociates to give such a species of higher entropy. The formation of such a molecule at high temperatures is consistent with the high internal energy that it possesses as a result of the poor overlap of the pi bonds, which was in turn explained by the inability of the phosphorus atoms to approach each other as closely as the smaller nitrogen atoms. The bond

101

length in the P_2 molecule is 1·89 Å, i.e. appreciably shorter than the normal single bond length found in the solid forms of the element. In an interesting experiment, Rice *et al.* heated phosphorus vapour to 1000° C to obtain diatomic molecules, and chilled the vapour to liquid nitrogen temperature by means of a cold finger. They obtained a brown deposit on the cold finger, which was very unstable and decomposed at about − 50° C to yield a mixture of white and red phosphorus. They believe that this brown material is the solid form of diatomic phosphorus obtained in a metastable condition, and able to polymerize when the temperature is allowed to rise.

The analogy of the preparation of this form with the preparation of white phosphorus by chilling vapour from a somewhat lower initial temperature, where the constitution is P_4, is very close. There is every reason to believe that this brown form is a genuine allotropic form of phosphorus.

The allotropy of **arsenic** has features in common with that of phosphorus, and is characterized by confused nomenclature of the various forms. When arsenic vapour is chilled to room temperature, or below, the element is obtained as a yellow solid which is soluble in, and can be recrystallized from, carbon disulphide as cubic crystals with a density of 2·0 g/cm³. This yellow arsenic is unstable and decomposes even at ordinary temperatures, particularly in the presence of light, although it can be stored at very low temperatures. It is isostructural with white phosphorus, but of higher internal energy.

The thermodynamically most stable form of the element, known as grey, or metallic, arsenic is obtained as rhombohedral crystals by cooling the liquid or condensing the vapour phase, provided that the temperature at which the crystals are allowed to grow is above 300° C. It sublimes at 633°, but is said to melt at 815° under a pressure of 36 atmospheres, and has a density much greater than that of the yellow form, i.e. 5·7 g/cm³. This form of the element shows metallic conduction.

The structure of this form of arsenic has been described in the previous Chapter (p. 67, Figs. 3.10, 3.11), and consists of infinite sheets in which each atom has three nearest neighbours. The inter-bond angle in this structure is smaller than that observed in black phosphorus, and both this decrease in angle and the ratio of distances to neighbours in the same and adjacent sheets, with increase in atomic number, was also discussed. The ratio has a value of 1·69 in the structure of black phosphorus, is 1·26 in this form of arsenic, and becomes 1·17 and 1·12 in the analogous forms of antimony and bismuth, as the metallic character increases. Thus the p character of the bonding increases, allowing more complete overlap as required for metallic conduction. As was pointed out in the previous section, the structure of grey arsenic is not identical

102

with that of black phosphorus and differs in the way in which the six-membered rings are fused.

Four further forms will be referred to more briefly. When yellow arsenic transforms on heating, or arsenic vapour is cooled to temperatures intermediate between 0° and 300°, it is possible to obtain forms known variously as amorphous grey (black) or mirror arsenic. Krebs has obtained a different form of the element, by heating in the presence of mercury, and believes this to be isostructural with the form of phosphorus obtained by the same procedure. Finally, a solution of yellow arsenic in carbon disulphide slowly deposits a brown substance at ordinary temperatures. It seems that the arguments advanced in the discussion of the transformations of phosphorus should be applicable again to arsenic, and that some at least of these various forms represent intermediate stages in the polymerization of the metastable yellow to the thermodynamically stable grey arsenic. The brown form is the most closely analogous to red phosphorus, being formed at relatively low temperatures, and thrown out of solution before the polymerization can proceed very far.

It seems worth while to quote from a text written forty years ago by Lavaux, concerning brown arsenic, since these remarks well express the ideas outlined above.

'C'est une forme amorphe, où l'on ne saurait voir un corps unique, nettement défini. C'est plutôt une classe de corps, paraissant provenir d'une polymérisation de l'arsenic jaune, ou d'une transformation qui le fait évoluer vers la forme métallique, et qui peut être plus ou moins complète ou profonde, suivant les conditions de leur naissance. Cette forme représenterait un premier stade intermédiaire, d'un degré un peu variable et imprécis, d'une stabilité qui semble précaire, dans la condensation de la matière arséniée, entre la forme précise arsenic jaune, où la densité est 2,03, et le groupe qui constitue un second stade, également mal défini, comprenant l'arsenic gris et l'arsenic vitreux miroitant, avec une densité voisine de 4,7, avant d'arriver à l'arsenic métallique, terme limite très net, où la densité atteint 5,7.'

Under these circumstances, it is perhaps preferable to consider that arsenic has only two allotropic forms, since the structural arrangements of the remaining forms are indefinite.

The parallel between arsenic and **antimony** is closer than that between arsenic and phosphorus. A yellow form which is believed to comprise Sb_4 molecules is obtained in a similar manner to yellow arsenic, but is stable only at still lower temperatures. The yellow product obtained by oxidation of stibine, SbH_3, is probably impure, and not a distinct form of the element. The normal stable, metallic form, can also be obtained in a manner analogous to metallic arsenic, and is iso-

103

morphous (isostructural) both with it and with bismuth. Amorphous grey material can also be obtained by the low temperature decomposition of the yellow form, or by the chilling of the vapour to an intermediate temperature.

The so-called explosive antimony, which is obtained when a strongly acid solution of an antimony halide is electrolysed, is an ill-defined material, sometimes referred to as an allotrope; it always contains an appreciable amount of halogen, and as an impure material of variable properties, it no longer warrants consideration as a separate allotropic form.

(*iv*) *The Group VI Elements*. The electronic configuration of elements in this group is $s^2 p^4$, and the $(8-N)$ rule requires that an atom of a Group VI element should have two nearest neighbours. The formation of two sigma bonds per atom is thus to be expected, and each atom therefore possesses two non-bonding pairs of electrons also.

The repeated formation of two bonds to nearest neighbours results in a long chain. If each atom uses four equivalent hybrid orbitals, an interbond angle of 109° 28′ should be found in such a chain, whereas decreasing s character in the bonding orbitals would cause a decrease towards the limiting value of 90° for pure p orbitals. Perfectly equivalent orbitals are not to be expected on account of the difference in spatial behaviour of a bonding pair and a non-bonding pair of electrons.

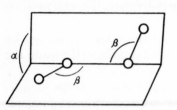

FIG. 4.12. The dihedral angle α and the interbond angle β required to completely define the geometry of a chain structure.

A chain possesses a greater degree of flexibility than a sheet, and in contrast to this latter, is not uniquely defined by an inter-bond angle; it is necessary also to define the angle of 'twist'. This angle, more correctly known as the dihedral angle, is defined as the angle between planes each of which contains three atoms—two atoms are common to both planes. A dihedral angle is illustrated in Fig. 4.12. In the liquid or gaseous state a chain is able to coil and uncoil, thus altering the value of the dihedral angle, but in the solid state it will be in an equilibrium position, such that repulsive forces of electron pairs upon each other will be minimized, and this corresponds to a fixed and definite dihedral angle.

Just as the Group V elements, some forms of the Group VI elements have the physical properties associated with small molecules. A small molecule can be a short open chain, or a short chain can have its extremities tied together to form a ring just as the bonds from a Group V element are tied together to form a tetrahedral molecule. Finally, a diatomic molecule in which each atom forms a sigma and a pi bond

104

instead of two sigma bonds, is possible, to be compared with nitrogen, and as an exception to the $(8 - N)$ rule.

The first element of the group, **oxygen**, continues the pattern set by nitrogen and graphite (carbon) in that its most stable form, i.e. of lowest internal energy, is stabilized by $p\pi$—$p\pi$ bonding; this diatomic molecule was discussed on p. 42. Like nitrogen, oxygen has allotropic forms in the solid state. The temperatures of transition between these forms are as indicated:

$$\alpha \underset{24°\text{K}}{\overset{\longrightarrow}{\longleftarrow}} \beta \underset{44°}{\overset{\longrightarrow}{\longleftarrow}} \gamma \underset{54°}{\overset{\longrightarrow}{\longleftarrow}} \text{Liquid}$$

In each form oxygen exists as diatomic molecules, so that the transitions must be of secondary coordination only, and of little chemical significance. It was suggested some years ago that the gamma form contained 'O_2—O_2 complexes', i.e. some of the intermolecular distances were slightly shorter than expected, and that this was evidence of the existence of a molecule O_4, but the evidence is not regarded as sufficiently convincing.

It will be seen below that sulphur exists as a diatomic molecule in the gaseous state at high temperatures, and as an S_8 cyclic molecule in the solid state, and it is a reasonable question to enquire why oxygen does not form a larger molecule in the solid state? The normal sigma bond length found for O—O, e.g. in hydrogen peroxide, is 1·49 Å and the length of the double bond, i.e. sigma and pi, in the oxygen molecule is 1·21 Å, whereas the corresponding values for sulphur are 2·05 and 1·89 Å respectively. Hence, the percentage shortening in sulphur is only 9%, compared with 18% for oxygen, when the double bond length is compared with the single bond. This illustrates the argument that the smaller atoms of the first-row elements can approach more closely to give stronger overlap and confer greater stability as a result of pi bonding, than the larger atoms of their heavier congeners. In consequence an oxygen atom forming two sigma bonds would result in a molecule of higher internal energy than if it forms one sigma and one pi bond, whereas the converse is true for sulphur. Hence, a larger molecule in which oxygen forms a chain or ring would not be formed at a temperature below that at which the diatomic molecule is stable, since a form of higher internal energy is produced by an increase of temperature.

The triatomic molecule of ozone, O_3, is an alternative form in which oxygen can be obtained. It is prepared from normal oxygen by various methods, each of which involves the input of energy, e.g. irradiation with u.v. light, the action of an electric discharge, or the electrolysis of suitable solutions. The amount of energy required to dissociate a molecule of oxygen, a necessary step in the formation of ozone, is 118 kcal/g-mol., whereas the wavelength of radiation required to produce the ozone is about 1900 Å, which corresponds to an energy of 150 kcal. The molecule of ozone is endoergic (requires an input of energy for its formation), i.e. of higher internal energy, approximately to the extent of the difference between these two amounts of energy. The molecule is formed as an alternative to straightforward reassociation when diatomic oxygen is dissociated under appropriate conditions, particularly at low temperatures, but always in relatively low percentage yield compared with the diatomic molecule.

Since the molecule is endoergic, ozone is metastable under all conditions, and decomposes to form diatomic oxygen, slowly at room temperature but rapidly at temperatures only slightly higher. Ozone is thus a monotropic species. It is unique for two allotropes to coexist in solid, liquid and gaseous states, so that a high energy barrier must impede the transition from the less stable ozone to the more stable oxygen.

Ozone has a melting point, when pure, of 23°K and a boiling point of 161°K; in contrast to oxygen it is diamagnetic. The shape of the molecule and the nature of the bonding have been discussed on p. 52. It is interesting to note that whereas nitrogen forms chains of atoms held together by double bonds in certain compounds, it cannot form an analogue to ozone.

The most significant chemical difference between the di- and triatomic species is the stronger oxidizing potential of the latter. When ozone acts as an oxidizing agent, its reaction product is diatomic oxygen, unless the oxidizable material can react with ordinary oxygen also; the oxidation by means of ozone is effectively oxidation by atomic oxygen preserved in reactive form by the metastability of the ozone molecule (though not as energetic or reactive as if it were uncombined). A further difference is that ozone can add to a $C=C$ to form an ozonide.

It is informative to point out that life on earth owes its existence to ozone; in the upper atmosphere, gaseous oxygen absorbs the u.v. radiation from the sun, and is thereby converted to ozone. This latter decomposes to a large extent before it can diffuse down to ground level, and accordingly is not normally detectable in our immediate atmosphere. If this absorption did not take place, the high energy radiation from the sun would burn up life on earth.

Sulphur is a yellow diamagnetic solid, with a melting point of 119°, and hence cannot be diatomic like oxygen. It is an element well known for the large number of allotropic forms in which it can be obtained. The enantiotropic change which takes place at 95·6°C is particularly well known, and the phase diagram of sulphur, including this transition, was discussed in detail in pp. 9–13.

The allotrope which is stable below the transition temperature, and hence at room temperature, is known as rhombic (it has an orthorhombic

106

unit cell) or alpha-sulphur. This is the thermodynamically stable form under normal conditions, and all the alternative forms are transformed to this after a sufficient interval of time. Rhombic sulphur is readily soluble in non-polar organic solvents, particularly carbon disulphide, and this solubility and the low melting point are consistent with a covalently bonded molecule of moderate molecular weight. The density of this form is $2 \cdot 07$ g/cm^3. The second allotrope, which is formed at and above the transition temperature of $95 \cdot 6°$, or by crystallization from the liquid in the temperature range between the melting point ($119°$) and the transition temperature, is known as monoclinic, prismatic or beta-sulphur. The density of this form is $1 \cdot 96$ g/cm^3, so that the change from the alpha to the beta form is accompanied by an appreciable increase in volume. The transition from one form to the other is not too rapid, so that the beta form can be maintained in metastable condition at normal temperature for some time, provided that no nuclei of the alpha form are present, or any stimulus applied, to initiate the transformation. It is said that at temperatures below $-30°$ transformation cannot occur, since the molecules have insufficient energy to migrate into alternative lattice positions.

A number of other forms of sulphur are also known in the solid state. These are all monotropic forms, and are metastable with respect to the alpha form under normal conditions. The first of these is nacreous or gamma-sulphur, first prepared and characterized by Gernez, and some-times known as Gernez' sulphur. This can be obtained by a number of different methods, such as the boiling of a saturated solution of sulphur in benzene, etc., for a number of hours, followed by slow cooling, or, alternatively, by the slow oxidation of an alcoholic solution of ammonium polysulphide. The physical properties of gamma-sulphur are not very different from those of the alpha form; the melting point is $107°$ and the density $2 \cdot 05$ g/cm^3. Like the beta form, it can be maintained for some time under normal conditions of temperature and pressure, but is metastable, and monotropic so that the change cannot be reversed except by the use of specific conditions such as those indicated above.

Another modification is rhombohedral or rho-sulphur, also known occasionally after its discoverer as Engel's sulphur. This form also can be prepared only under certain carefully controlled conditions. Thus, it is obtained when a saturated aqueous solution of sodium thiosulphate is added to a concentrated solution of hydrochloric acid at $10°$, and the precipitate so obtained extracted with chloroform. The crystals obtained from this solution have a density of $2 \cdot 21$ g/cm^3 and their melting point is less than $100°$.

It is convenient to consider the available structural information about these forms, which are characterized by their solubility in non-polar solvents, before discussing the nature of 'insoluble' varieties of sulphur. The structure of alpha, rhombic, sulphur has been known for some time to comprise puckered eight-membered rings, in the crown form (see Fig. 4.13). The vapour in equilibrium with the solid also contains these eight-membered rings, and molecular weight determinations on solutions of alpha-sulphur in carbon disulphide similarly indicate S_8 units. The S—S bond length in the molecule is 2·05 Å, and the inter-bond angle is 107° 55'; since the molecule is rigid, these parameters define the dihedral angle precisely, and this has a value of 98° 39'. The length of the S—S bond corresponds to a pure sigma bond with no pi character, and the inter-bond angle is relatively close to the tetrahedral angle required for four equivalent sp^3 hybrid orbitals, closer than the values observed in any form of the neighbouring element, phosphorus.

The structure of the beta form has not, apparently, been determined, but since it also exists in equilibrium with vapour containing S_8 rings, and the energy of transformation between the alpha and beta forms is small, it is believed that this form differs from the alpha form only in the manner in which the molecules are arranged in the crystal. The structure of gamma sulphur is known to consist of puckered eight-membered rings but packed in a different manner from those in the crystal of the alpha form.

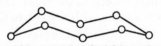

FIG. 4.13. A puckered eight-membered ring as in alpha-sulphur.

The structure of rho-sulphur, on the other hand, consists of puckered six-membered rings, in the chair form. The bond length is 2·06 Å and the bond angle significantly smaller than in alpha-sulphur, i.e. 102°; this results in a dihedral angle of 75°.

There is not an appreciable difference in the internal energies of sulphur rings and sulphur chains, and it will be seen that the transformation from rings to chains becomes thermodynamically necessary at a temperature which is not appreciably above the melting point, i.e. in the liquid phase. It is reasonable to enquire, however, why sulphur should adopt an eight-membered ring rather than six- or ten-membered in its most stable form. Since a S—S single bond length is effectively constant, the parameters which can vary with change in ring size are the inter-bond angle and the dihedral angle. The inter-bond angle is unlikely to be outside the range 90°–109° 28', i.e. the extremes required by pure p and sp^3 hybrid orbitals respectively. It is less immediately obvious what value to assume as optimum for the dihedral angle. In a molecule which has more freedom, and does not have the rigidity of a ring, it is reasonable to assume that the dihedral angle adopted will be such as to minimize any repulsive forces within the molecule, particularly

108

the interaction of non-bonding pairs of electrons with each other and with bonding pairs. A survey of other sulphur-containing compounds shows that a dihedral angle within the range 90°–100° is frequently found. Assuming a reasonable inter-bond angle, calculations can then be made to determine which ring size is in accord with the smallest deviations from this range of dihedral angle. Such calculations were made first by Pauling, and later refined by Donohue *et al.*, who found that the stability of the various ring sizes is:

$$S_8 > S_6 > S_{10} > S_4$$

It is in accord with this that the thermodynamically stable alpha form contains eight-membered rings, and that the only other ring size to be positively identified in the solid state is the six-membered, although it is unstable with respect to the eight-membered ring.

In view of this discussion it is pertinent to enquire why the six-membered ring can be formed. As was pointed out earlier a particular preparative method is necessary, i.e. interaction of solutions of thio-sulphate and hydrogen ion. Bartlett and his co-workers have studied this problem and suggest that the kinetics of the reaction are consistent with a series of displacements of SO_3^{2-} by $S_2O_3^{2-}$ leading to the formation of an increasingly long ion of type $HS_xSO_3^-$, as shown by the equations:

$$2S_2O_3^{2-} \xrightarrow{\text{H}^+} HS_3O_3^- + SO_3^{2-}$$

$$HS_3O_3^- + S_2O_3^{2-} \longrightarrow HS_4O_3^- + SO_3^{2-} \quad \text{etc.}$$

When $x = 6$, an intramolecular displacement,

$$^-S_6.SO_3^- \longrightarrow S_6 + SO_3^{2-}$$

can occur through a sterically favoured cyclic transition state, to give a six-membered ring. Simultaneous reactions lead to the formation of polythionic acids up to the $H_2S_6O_6$ which also contains six inter-linked sulphur atoms, and polysulphides, etc. There may well be other specific structures, known or as yet unknown, which owe their existence to a particular steric mechanism.

The mechanism for the transformation from alpha- to beta- sulphur, and *vice versa*, and that from gamma to alpha involve no change in the primary coordination and take place with relative ease. The transformation from the rhombohedral (rho) form to the alpha form, however, involves a change in molecular complexity, i.e. from six- to eight-membered rings, and such a change must be a more difficult one. The transformation in the solid state is indeed slow, when compared with the other transformations referred to above, and it is a feature of this change that polymeric, insoluble, material is formed in addition to the normal alpha form. A further feature of rho-sulphur, in which it differs from the other metastable gamma form, is that it can be recovered from solution unchanged, whereas a solution of the gamma form must deposit the stable alpha form. The action of a non-polar solvent is not sufficiently drastic to effect immediately a change, which must involve a ring-opening. It will be more convenient to return to the mechanism of transformation of rho-sulphur later in the section (see p. 116).

There are at least two further forms of sulphur, which have not been considered so far, and which are insoluble in solvents such as carbon

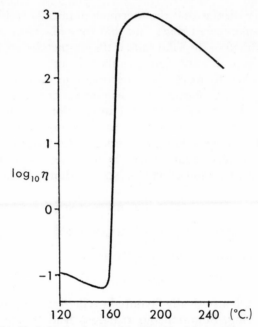

Fig. 4.14. Variation in viscosity (η) of liquid sulphur with temperature.

disulphide. Particular reference must be made to the so-called plastic and purple sulphur; the former is obtained by chilling liquid sulphur, and the latter by chilling the vapour from high temperature, and it is necessary in order to understand these, to discuss in some detail the nature of both liquid and gaseous sulphur.

Molten sulphur at temperatures just above the melting point (119°) is a highly mobile liquid. A plot of viscosity against temperature, however, shows an extremely rapid and sharp change at a temperature of 159°; the viscosity of the liquid suddenly becomes so great that it is not possible to pour it from its container by inversion. The viscosity continues to rise until a maximum is reached at about 195° after which it falls steadily

110

(see Fig. 4.14). It is hardly surprising that other physical properties should undergo a marked change at the same temperature; one example is the specific heat, and its variation with temperature is shown in Fig. 4.15. This behaviour is interpreted as due to a monomer–polymer transformation, and one feature of note is that the changes observed take place independently of time, from which it is concluded that the equilibrium in the liquid is able to adjust itself very rapidly to any changes in external conditions.

It is now appropriate to discuss the nature of the changes observed. In the temperature range from the melting point to approximately 155° C the only species present in the melt is the molecule S_8 which is present also in the solid state. These relatively small, approximately spherical molecules of the monomer can slide over one another quite

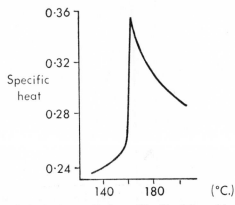

FIG. 4.15. Variation in the specific heat of liquid sulphur with temperature.

readily, so that the resistance to flow, or viscosity, of the liquid is low, and as is normal for liquids decreases with increase in temperature, as the molecules acquire more thermal energy. The temperature of 159° is the critical one at which polymer can form, i.e. the free energies of formation of monomer and polymer are the same, and the large change in the specific heat at this temperature indicates that heat is being absorbed to effect the transformation, i.e. latent heat. The break in the specific heat curve starts two or three degrees before 159°, and thus before the sharp rise in viscosity, and it has been suggested that this is caused by the formation of rings larger than S_8. Since these are also approximately spherical, no marked change in viscosity is likely.

At 159° polymerization occurs with the breaking of rings and the formation of long-chain molecules. These can coil themselves up into complicated patterns, become intertwined and hence unable to slide over each other, so that the viscosity of the melt becomes very high. The

111

behaviour of liquid sulphur at temperatures above 159° is that of a solution of a polymer in a monomer, the relative amounts of the two forms varying with temperature. The viscosity of the solvent monomer will continue to decrease with increase in temperature in the normal way, but Fig. 4.14 indicates a further increase, before the final steady decrease in viscosity is observed. The measured viscosity is not that of monomer or polymer in isolation, but of the equilibrium mixture, so that the increase to a maximum value, which is observed, must be due to the behaviour of the polymer.

Immediately above the polymerization temperature, the concentration of the polymer would be expected to be relatively low, and the average chain length relatively short. As the temperature continues to

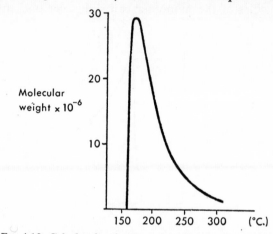

FIG. 4.16. Calculated molecular weight of the sulphur polymer.

increase the average chain length also increases initially, so that its solution in the monomer will become more viscous. Eventually the large amount of thermal energy supplied to the system causes the chains to break down into smaller fragments, and as the average chain length falls, so also will the viscosity of the solution. The rise in the viscosity as temperature increases followed by its subsequent decrease can thus be explained by competition between two processes; (i) an increase in chain length or increasing degree of polymerization (as polymerization becomes energetically more favourable) and (ii) a decrease in chain length as the thermal energy becomes larger. It follows that the average molecular weight of the polymer must pass through a maximum at a temperature near to that at which the maximum viscosity is observed. A calculation of the variation in molecular weight has been made by Eisenberg and Tobolsky; the results are shown in Fig. 4.16. It can be seen that the maximum chain length reached corresponds with a molecular

112

weight of about 30×10^6, i.e. a chain length of about one million atoms. At each end of a polymer chain there must be an unused valency, i.e. an unpaired electron, presumably in a pi orbital; careful measurement has detected the magnetic properties to be expected from such unpaired electrons, so that the hypothesis that these infinite chains join together at their extremities to form an infinitely large ring, must be considered untenable. A graph of the percentage composition by weight of the

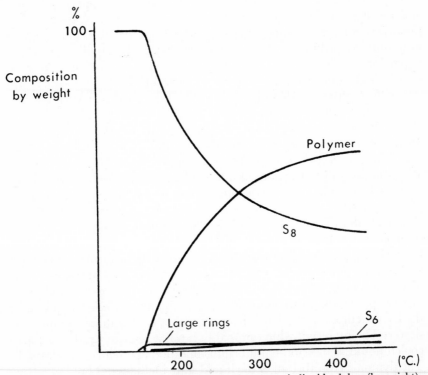

Fig. 4.17. Percentage composition of various species present in liquid sulphur (by weight).

various species present in liquid sulphur, calculated by Gee, is shown in Fig. 4.17.

The mechanism for the polymerization of octatomic rings to form chains requires as an initial stage the breaking of an S—S bond, i.e. ring-opening, with the formation of an eight-membered chain which has an unpaired electron, i.e. free radical character, at each end. When two of these chains join together to form a longer chain a new S—S bond is formed. When n rings are broken, n S—S bonds are broken, and when these fragments combine to form an infinite chain $(n-1)$ S—S bonds are re-formed. Since n is normally very large, n can be regarded as equal to

113

$(n-1)$, and it can be said that the number of bonds broken and the number re-formed are the same. In the reverse process, as liquid sulphur is cooled, the fission of S—S bonds allows the formation of octatomic rings, and re-formation of S—S bonds. The latent heat of transformation, corresponding to the difference in internal energies of the two forms, which differ in the secondary coordination of the two molecules, is about 400 cal/g-atom.

Sulphur boils at a temperature of $444°$ C under atmospheric pressure, and the vapour formed comprises cyclic S_8 molecules. At higher temperatures smaller molecules such as S_4 and S_6 are believed to be present in dynamic equilibrium with S_8, the position of the equilibrium being dependent not only upon temperature but also on pressure. At sufficiently high temperatures diatomic S_2 molecules also are formed, and above $900°$ represent the sole constituent of the vapour. (At still higher temperatures, dissociation to atomic sulphur occurs.) This molecule is the analogue of oxygen, and its occurrence only as a high temperature form has been discussed previously (see p. 105).

It is now appropriate to consider the remaining solid forms of sulphur. When liquid sulphur is poured into cold water, the well-known plastic sulphur is obtained. When this material is freshly prepared it is amorphous to X-rays, and largely insoluble in those solvents which dissolve rhombic sulphur, etc. On standing it gradually becomes brittle, losing its plastic or rubbery nature, and transforms to alpha-sulphur. This formation of plastic sulphur is a process similar to the formation of white and brown phosphorus, yellow arsenic and yellow antimony, etc., whereby a high temperature equilibrium is 'frozen' by rapid chilling, i.e. it is prevented from adjusting itself to the new position required by the lower temperature, which it would attain if the rate of cooling were slower. The material, which probably is not a solid but rather a supercooled liquid, is in a non-equilibrium condition and hence is metastable. The dynamic equilibrium of the liquid state includes not only S_8 solvent molecules, but also polymeric molecules of varying chain length in random orientation, so that it is hardly surprising that plastic sulphur does not give a regular X-ray pattern, since this requires an ordered structure. The transformation to alpha-sulphur is in accord with the metastability of this form.

If the plastic material is stretched, it becomes a crystalline solid, and the crystalline material, called fibrous sulphur, can be kept for some time at room temperature without change. Some of this material is soluble in carbon disulphide, but much is not. An X-ray study of this crystalline material reveals an unusual and particularly subtle atomic pattern. The principal feature of the structure is of infinite chains of atoms each arranged in the form of a helix; the repeat distance of this helix is 13.7Å,

114

which accommodates ten atoms arranged in three complete turns. In this helical chain, the S—S distance is 2·04 Å, the inter-bond angle 107° and the dihedral angle 87°; of these values, only that of the dihedral angle is significantly different from those of alpha-sulphur, and the deviation of this is less than is found in rho-sulphur. The helices pack together in a close-packed manner as parallel cylinders, *cf.* Fig. 3.15. The fibrous appearance of the material is in accord with this structural pattern; such a 'giant' molecule would be insoluble, and hence is the residue after the extraction of the crystalline material with carbon disulphide.

The full subtlety of the structure becomes apparent when the distribution of the 'soluble' portion of the material is considered. The spaces between the coils of the helices are of precisely the appropriate size to

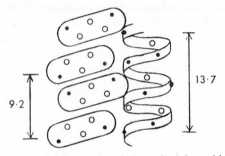

Fig. 4.18. The intercalation of eight-membered rings of sulphur within the helical coils of sulphur chains as found in fibrous sulphur. The open circles represent atoms nearer to the eye, and dots atoms beneath the plane of the others. The repeat unit of the ring structure is exactly $\frac{2}{3}$ that of the chain, so that some coincidence in X-ray patterns results. (After Prins *et al.*)

accommodate eight-membered rings, and these were present in the liquid from which the material originated. The cyclic molecules are intercalated into these interstices, and are thus held in a definite orientation which is that of gamma-sulphur. The complete X-ray pattern can therefore be resolved into two constituent parts, the one due to the chains and the other to the rings. Treatment with solvent leaches out the small molecules, which can be crystallized as alpha-sulphur, and leaves behind the insoluble skeleton of the chains (Fig. 4.18).

The tangle in which the ring molecules (known as lambda-sulphur) and the chains (known as mu-sulphur) are present in the liquid state is preserved when the liquid is chilled, but ordered structure is established when plastic sulphur is submitted to a stretching force. Since the chain molecules are stable only above 159°, the fibrous sulphur is metastable with respect to alpha-sulphur, but the transformation in the solid state is more difficult than in the liquid, so is relatively slow. This transformation can be compared with that of white phosphorus to polymeric material, though in the reverse direction.

115

The transformation from rho- to alpha-sulphur, which involves change from S_6 to S_8 rings, has features in common with the transformation from the chain structure to a ring structure as described above. The initial step is a ring-opening and S—S bond fission. The formation of an octatomic ring is possible only if the six-membered fragments first combine to form a longer chain and then break down once more, and this process in the solid state is also likely to be a difficult one, and hence slow. Once the transformation has begun, at any instant of time until it is quite complete, there is likely to be present a mixture of unchanged rho-sulphur, transformed alpha-sulphur, and some chain molecules formed as intermediate. This intermediate accounts for the observation that rho-sulphur as it transforms yields both soluble and insoluble material, although after sufficient time the insoluble material also should transform to the thermodynamically stable form. The transformation from a six-membered ring to an eight-membered ring has also been studied in solution in carbon disulphide. (It was pointed out previously that rho-sulphur could be recrystallized unchanged from this solvent.) The transformation has been found by Bartlett *et al.* to be catalysed by such species as HS^- and HSO_3^-, both of which are described as thiophilic reagents, i.e. they have an affinity to bond to a sulphur atom, and thus facilitate the ring-opening. The action of such catalysts can be compared with the addition of iodine, etc., to catalyse the ring-opening of the P_4 molecule as the first stage in the polymerization of that element.

The second insoluble form of sulphur, referred to on p. 110, is purple sulphur. This was obtained by Rice and Sparrow by a technique analogous to that used for the preparation of brown phosphorus (p. 102). Thus they chilled sulphur vapour from a temperature of about 1000° C to liquid nitrogen temperature. This purple material is said to be insoluble in carbon disulphide, but the temperature of this experiment must have been extremely low, and the observation of doubtful validity, since purple sulphur is found to decompose rapidly when it is allowed to heat up from the temperature of liquid nitrogen. The products of this decomposition are alpha-sulphur and some insoluble material, which is presumably polymeric in nature. Purple sulphur was found to be paramagnetic.

There is little doubt that this material is a genuine metastable allotrope of sulphur, and contains diatomic molecules S_2, which are known to exist in the gaseous phase at high temperatures, and which are, like oxygen, paramagnetic. It is formed as are various metastable allotropes, by freezing a high temperature equilibrium, and thus isolating the high temperature component at low temperatures. The decomposition products reported are as would be expected from this dimeric molecule. As it polymerizes rapidly, a mixture of ring and chain molecules should result, though this product should transform after an interval of time

116

to 100% alpha-sulphur. Rice and Sparrow looked for evidence of the presence of molecules such as S_4 and S_6 in their product, but without success. This negative evidence cannot be taken as proving their absence either in the purple material, or even less, in the gaseous state.

Various other forms of sulphur have been claimed, but whereas those forms considered above are well characterized and worthy of the term allotrope, it seems likely that the remaining materials, most of which are insoluble and amorphous, represent various stages of polymerization, without the long-range order which gives rise to X-ray patterns.

Just as arsenic has features in common with phosphorus, but differs from it in many ways, the same remark applies to **selenium** with respect to sulphur. The thermodynamically most stable form of selenium, known as grey selenium, can be obtained by crystallization from the molten element, or by condensation of the vapour, provided that the temperature at which the crystals are allowed to form is not far below the melting point of 220°. This form is insoluble in carbon disulphide, etc., and is the most dense form of the element, i.e. 4·8 g/cm.³ The other forms of the element transform spontaneously to give grey selenium, particularly when heated. The most important property is that it behaves as a semiconductor, and is the only form of the element to have this property; the energy gap is about 1·8 eV compared with a value of 0·35 eV for the corresponding form of tellurium and the metallic conduction of polonium (*cf.* pp. 52 and 94).

If a lower temperature is used for condensation of vapour or liquid, an amorphous material is obtained, known as vitreous or black selenium, which is commercially available. This form has a sparing solubility in carbon disulphide, a density slightly lower than that of the grey form, 4·3 g/cm³, and is not a semiconductor. When heated, it transforms quite readily to the more stable grey form. Solutions of vitreous selenium in carbon disulphide deposit red crystals. According to the exact conditions used it is possible to obtain one or other of two crystalline forms, both belonging to the monoclinic system, but with unit cells which differ slightly in size. They are referred to as alpha-monoclinic and beta-monoclinic respectively. The density of these forms is 4.45 g/cm³; they are, of course, soluble in carbon disulphide, and are not semiconductors; on heating, each form yields grey selenium by a monotropic change. Finally, an amorphous red form is obtained by chemical reduction of solutions of selenites. This form is said to change to the crystalline red form on heating below about 70°, but the grey form if heated to a higher temperature.

Grey selenium consists of infinite chains packed closely together as was referred to in the discussion on p. 68 *et seq.* The distance between two selenium atoms in a chain is 2·32 Å, whereas the nearest neighbour in an adjacent chain is at a distance of 3·46 Å, i.e. a ratio of 1·49. This

117

can be compared with a corresponding ratio of 1·22 in tellurium, in illustration of the point noted previously (pp. 51, 63, 102) that as metallic character increases, neighbouring chains become closer together. The chains form a spiral which repeats after three atoms, so that the dihedral angle is 120°. The relationship of this structure to the sodium chloride lattice was pointed out in the previous Chapter, and this structure was seen to contain six-membered rings, in the chair form.

The two red forms of selenium both comprise buckled eight-membered rings in the crown form, directly analogous with those of sulphur. The bond length is 2·34 Å and the bond angle 105° in both forms; a slightly larger bond length than in sulphur is to be expected from the larger atoms, and the decrease in bond angle is consistent with the trend towards pure p bonds in the heavier elements, which has been referred to previously. The two forms differ in the orientation of the molecules with respect to each other but must be very similar in energy. Both are metastable with respect to the grey form, and the transformation from one red form to the other does not seem to have been observed. The input of energy to either form causes transformation to the grey form rather than to the alternative red form.

The grey and red crystalline forms are well characterized allotropes with the polymer-monomer structural relationship of fibrous and rhombic sulphur, but with a closer thermodynamic relationship to black and white phosphorus. Thus the polymeric form is the more stable thermodynamically in the solid state, whereas this is not the case with the various forms of sulphur. Similarly, the amorphous red and black forms of selenium are analogous with red phosphorus and represent intermediate stages in the polymerization; amorphous red selenium presumably is closer to crystalline red, and vitreous black to crystalline grey. The vitreous form is believed variously to contain small rings such as Se_6, larger rings, short chains or long chains, and the existence of such different constituents in the liquid phase has been suggested. There is certainly less agreement on these aspects of the behaviour than on the corresponding aspects of the behaviour of sulphur.

In contrast to sulphur, liquid selenium shows no anomaly of viscosity, and its behaviour can be explained by postulating a temperature-dependent equilibrium between ring molecules of various sizes, e.g. six- and eight-membered. When it crystallizes slowly near the melting point, polymeric grey selenium with its regular structure is formed. During solidification at temperatures well below the melting point the atoms have insufficient thermal energy to arrange themselves in this way, and the vitreous form is obtained which may have the ordered polymer structure in the short range but not in the long range. It is said

118

that when the liquid is chilled to very low temperatures, a mixture of cyclic molecules and polymer results, and this is possible provided that some polymerization can occur during the cooling process. When vitreous selenium is treated with carbon disulphide, some of it dissolves. This is the part of the material present as Se_8 rings which has not undergone polymerization during the cooling from the liquid state.

This interpretation of the behaviour of selenium seems to be in accord with the behaviour of the other p block elements; the important difference between sulphur and selenium is that the octatomic sulphur molecule is slightly the more stable in the normal temperature range, whereas the polymeric form of selenium is the more stable.

In contrast to sulphur and selenium, tellurium has one crystalline form only, possessing the chain structure of grey selenium, with which it is isomorphous. The closer approach of the chains, and the smaller gap between its energy bands, such that it is intermediate between selenium and polonium has been noted above.

Polonium has two allotropic modifications, referred to as alpha and beta. The alpha form is rhombohedral with an inter-axial angle of $98°\ 13'$, whereas the beta form is simple cubic. The structure of beta-polonium is that of sodium chloride, where both lattices are occupied by the same kind of atom (p. 67), and can also be regarded, as was discussed previously, as chains packed so closely that the interatomic distance between the chains is the same as the interatomic distance within the same chain. The alpha form can be regarded as a minor distortion of the beta form, tending towards the structure of tellurium; the cell lengths of the two forms are almost identical. This element, like plutonium, etc., is difficult to study on account of radioactivity. It is self-heating, and rapidly contaminates itself with its daughter product, lead. Exact thermal studies are difficult because of the emission of heat, and the presence of an impurity can affect transition temperatures. The transition from one form to the other is reversible from a structural point of view, but the temperatures at which transition has been observed to start differ according to direction, viz.

$$\alpha \underset{18°\,C}{\overset{54°\,C}{\rightleftharpoons}} \beta$$

The element behaves as a metallic conductor.

(*v*) *The Group VII Elements.* The electronic configuration of elements in this group is s^2p^5, and the $(8 - N)$ rule requires than an atom of a Group VII element should have one nearest neighbour only, resulting in the formation of diatomic molecules. This allows differences only in the ways that the molecules are stacked together in the crystal, i.e. changes in secondary coordination.

119

An enantiotropic allotropic transformation has been observed between two different forms of **fluorine** at a temperature of $45 \cdot 6°$ K, but no structural data are available. There is also some evidence for the existence of a metastable form of **iodine**, of monoclinic space group in contrast to the normal orthorhombic form; it is formed under conditions of vacuum distillation, but cannot be regarded as definitely established.

No allotropic forms of the solidified monatomic inert gases of Group VIII are known.

CHAPTER 5

VARIANT FORMS OF GASEOUS ELEMENTS

The formation of active nitrogen and *para*-hydrogen and their existence at normal temperatures will be discussed in this section. On occasion, each has been regarded as an allotropic modification but the definition given in Chapter 1 does not include them as such; active nitrogen is not obtainable as a pure species in the solid state, whereas *ortho*- and *para*-hydrogen should have identical arrangements of their diatomic molecules in their crystal structures.

A discussion of these particular forms of nitrogen and hydrogen is included because of their particular chemical significance. There are features of the behaviour of each which are very similar to features of certain of the allotropic species considered previously.

The atomic spectra of certain elements show details of structure which can be explained only by the assumption that some nuclei, like electrons, possess spin. The effect of nuclear spin is seen also in molecular rotational spectra. A molecule composed of two identical atoms, each of which possesses nuclear spin, can exist in two forms according as the nuclear spins are parallel or anti-parallel. These are known as *ortho* and *para* respectively. The rotational energy levels of molecules are quantized, and it is found that the even quantum states correspond to the spectrum of one form, whereas the odd quantum states correspond to that of the other. If *ortho* and *para* forms are present in equal proportions in a mixture, alternate lines in the spectrum are of equal intensity, whereas, the spectrum of one pure form comprises only half as many lines as the spectrum of the mixture.

As the temperature falls, the population of the higher rotational energy levels decreases, and that of the lower levels increases, since the molecules have a decreasing amount of thermal energy; finally, at the absolute zero of temperature, all molecules should be in the lowest possible energy level. That level is the zero quantum state. The energies of the *ortho* and *para* forms are not identical, and the form which is thermodynamically the more stable at $0° K$ is that which occupies the zero quantum state; at higher temperatures this form corresponds to the even quantum states, the actual value of the nuclear spin determining whether this form is the *ortho* or *para*.

Ortho and *para* forms should exist, theoretically, for the molecules $^1H_2$ and $^2H_2$ (or D_2), $^{14}N_2$ and $^{35}Cl_2$. It should be possible in principle to

121

obtain the low temperature form of any of these in a pure state, but not the high temperature form. Both forms exist together in equilibrium, but there is a definite temperature above which the equilibrium composition of the mixture does not change, and only below this temperature, which becomes lower as the molecular weight increases, can an enhanced concentration of the low temperature form be obtained. In the case of the latter two molecules, this temperature lies below their melting points, so that the interconversion cannot occur and the separate forms have not been observed.

ORTHO- AND PARA-HYDROGEN

Normal hydrogen at room temperature contains 25% of the *para* form and 75% of the *ortho* form, and this composition does not alter with increase in temperature. The *ortho* form cannot be prepared in the pure

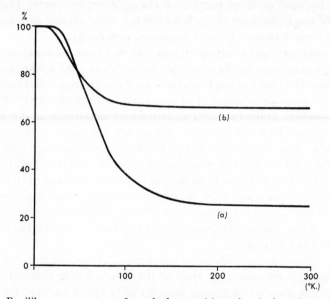

FIG. 5.1. Equilibrum percentage of *para*-hydrogen, (*a*), and *ortho*-deuterium, (*b*), plotted against temperature.

state. The *para* form is that which corresponds to the even quantum states, and hence is the more thermodynamically stable at the absolute zero of temperature. At temperatures between absolute zero and room temperature the two forms can exist in equilibrium with each other, the proportion of the *ortho* form increasing with temperature, as shown in Fig. 5.1. Above room temperature, both forms exist in equilibrium, but the position of this no longer varies. Normal hydrogen can be kept for

122

some time at low temperatures, as can *para*-hydrogen at normal temperatures, i.e. under non-equilibrium conditions, because the transformation from one form to another is slow except in the presence of a catalyst.

Since the two forms differ in energy, they differ also in physical properties, e.g. the melting and boiling points of *para*-hydrogen are about $0 \cdot 1°$ lower than those of normal hydrogen; use is made of the difference in thermal conductivity of the two forms to analyse mixtures.

Conversion from one form to another means, in general, the conversion of a certain proportion of the molecules present in a sample to allow the establishment of the equilibrium composition required by new experimental conditions; it refers particularly to the conversion of the low temperature *para* form to the normal temperature equilibrium mixture of 75% *ortho*. Conversion is effected by hydrogen atoms, paramagnetic substances, or surfaces on which hydrogen can be adsorbed. The presence of hydrogen atoms, produced thermally, photochemically or by electric discharge, affords the possibility of an exchange mechanism where bonds are broken and reformed in equal number. The equation for such a conversion is given below, along with that for hydrogen–deuterium exchange, which takes place presumably by the same mechanism, with similar kinetics under similar conditions.

$$pH_2 + H = oH_2 + H \qquad (5.1)$$

$$D_2 + H = HD + D \qquad (5.2)$$

As a result of this exchange mechanism, hydrogen molecules are continually being formed, and hence an equilibrium condition results. The conversion of *para* to normal hydrogen is a method for the detection of hydrogen atoms.

Paramagnetic substances such as nitric oxide, oxygen, or ions of transition or lanthanide metals also bring about conversion. Paramagnetic materials contain unpaired electrons, i.e. electrons which are not paired with an electron of compensating (opposite) spin, and it is likely that conversion is effected by the perturbation due to the spins of these unpaired electrons. The rate of conversion, under comparable conditions, is dependent upon the magnetic moment, so that under comparable conditions, the rate of reaction falls in the following sequence of catalysts, $Mn(II) > Fe(II) > Co(II) > Ni(II) > Cu(II) > Zn(II)$. The number of unpaired electrons falls from five to zero in this series. Paramagnetic materials do not bring about hydrogen–deuterium exchange. The detection of unpaired electrons, e.g. in free radicals, can, like the detection of hydrogen atoms, be accomplished by following the conversion of *para*-hydrogen.

123

Para-hydrogen conversion also occurs on the surface of a catalyst, particularly a metal. This process may involve the dissociation of a molecule into atoms, followed by their adsorption on two separate sites on the metal surface, desorption and recombination; alternatively, there may be exchange between a hydrogen atom chemically bound on the surface and a molecule more loosely held on top of the chemisorbed hydrogen atoms—a mechanism similar to the homogeneous exchange reaction considered above. In either case, the continuous breaking and re-formation of bonds leads to a mixture of the equilibrium composition. Once again hydrogen–deuterium exchange can take place by the same mechanism.

The uncatalysed conversion from one form to the other, which can be regarded as the twisting of one nuclear spin, is a slow process, even at high temperatures, although if the temperature is sufficiently high to allow dissociation, conversion occurs readily. The various mechanisms for conversion recall the mechanisms whereby one solid allotrope is transformed to another by a distillative process or via an intermediate in solution.

ACTIVE NITROGEN

The name 'active nitrogen' is given to the product obtained when gaseous nitrogen at low pressures is subjected to an electrical discharge. A yellow-orange glow is emitted which persists for several minutes after the discharge has been switched off. Studies of active nitrogen have, of necessity, been largely of a spectroscopic nature, and these readily show up lines caused by the presence of even traces of impurities; this explains, at least in part, the comment of a recent reviewer that 'Studies (of active nitrogen) have been marked as perhaps no other chemical endeavour with a plethora of disagreement, contradictory data, and general scientific frustration'. It has been established, however, that the 'active' component of the afterglow is atomic nitrogen, in its ground state.

The recombination of nitrogen atoms to form molecules seems to involve collision with a third body, and such three-body collisions cannot be of frequent occurrence at the low pressures at which active nitrogen is formed. Hence, some time is required for the complete disappearance of the nitrogen atoms. Although reaction with a second nitrogen atom is not instantaneous, a nitrogen atom can combine with other molecules and such reactions have been much studied. The free nitrogen atom possesses an appreciable amount of available energy, and this energy facilitates reactions which could not take place otherwise. This is the justification for the adjective 'active'.

Reactions with organic molecules invariably yield HCN as the principal product, whereas ammonia is seldom, if ever, detected. This

124

suggests that the nitrogen atom attacks carbon rather than hydrogen. Both degradation and polymerization reactions occur in addition to the formation of hydrogen cyanide. Two reactions with inorganic molecules can also be mentioned as illustration. Thus with nitric oxide, the primary reaction is $N + NO = N_2 + O$; if insufficient nitric oxide is added, the oxygen and nitrogen atoms can combine to form more nitric oxide. Secondly, reaction with phosphine yields hydrogen and a polymeric phosphorus nitride, but not apparently any polymeric phosphorus as might be expected when the hydrogen is abstracted from phosphine. Further chemical reactions have been investigated, particularly by Winkler and his school, *q.v.*

Although some comparison with diatomic sulphur molecules in purple sulphur can be made, active nitrogen is not considered an allotrope since it cannot be obtained pure, nor in the solid state; it does not seem warranted to consider this as an allotrope any more than any other element which can be obtained under some conditions as free atoms in the gaseous state.

SUGGESTED FURTHER READING

A. Findlay, *The Phase Rule*, Dover Publications, 1951.

Phase Transformations in Solids, Wiley, 1951.

P. Pascal ed., *Nouveau Traité de Chimie Minérale*, Masson et Co.

F. H. Spedding and A. H. Daane, *The Rare Earths*, Wiley, 1961.

H. Krebs, 'Inorganic High Polymers', *Angew. Chem.*, 1958, **70**, 615.

H. Krebs *et al.*, 'The Catalytic Preparation of black Phosphorus', *Z. anorg. Chem.*, 1955, **280**, 119.

G. Gee, 'Sulphur—a Survey of Recent Work on the Physical Chemistry of the Element', *Sci. Progr.*, 1955, **43**, 193.

A. von Hippel, 'Structure and Conductivity in Group VI of the Periodic Table', *J. Phys. Chem.*, 1948, **16**, 372.

P. D. Bartlett *et al.*, 'Reactions of Elemental Sulphur—Part V', *J. Amer. Chem. Soc.*, 1961, **83** 109.

J. Donohue *et al.*, 'The Crystal and Molecular Structure of S_6', *J. Amer. Chem. Soc.*, 1961, **83** 3748.

W. Rudorff, 'Graphite Intercalation Compounds', *Adv. Inorg. Chem. Radiochem.*, 1959, **1**, 224.

J. L. Hoard and A. E. Newkirk, 'An Analysis of Polymorphism in Boron based upon X-ray Diffraction Results', *J. Amer. Chem. Soc.*, 1960, **82**, 70.

INDEX

The allotropy of individual elements is indexed under the appropriate element; in general, allotropes are not listed individually.

129